North Reef ⊙

Tryon I. ⊛

North-⊛ ⬭ Wilson I.⊙ ⬭ Broomfield Reef
West Island ⊙ Wreck I.

CAPRICORN GROUP

Tropic Heron I. ⬭ of Sykes Reef Capricorn

Erskine I. ⊛ Wistari Reef ⬭ One Tree I.

⊛⬭ Masthead I.
Irving ⬭ Polmaise Reef
Reef

Lamont Reef
Fitzroy Reef

Llewellyn Reef

BUNKER GROUP ⬭ Boult Reef
Hoskyn I. ⊛

Fairfax I. ⊛
Lady Musgrave I. ⬭

N

W ——————— E

S

WONDERS OF THE
GREAT BARRIER REEF

A CORAL GARDEN

Wonders of the GREAT BARRIER REEF

By
T. C. ROUGHLEY, B.Sc., F.R.Z.S.,

Superintendent of Fisheries, New South Wales; President of the
Royal Zoological Society of New South Wales, 1934-6; President
of the Linnean Society of New South Wales, 1938-9.
Author of *The Cult of the Goldfish*

*With Fifty-two Natural-colour Photographs
by the Author*

ANGUS & ROBERTSON LIMITED
SYDNEY :: LONDON
1945

*Set up, printed and bound
in Australia by
Halstead Press Pty Limited
9-19 Nickson Street, Sydney
1945*

*Registered in Australia for
transmission through the
post as a book*

PREFACE

THE Great Barrier Reef of Australia is one of the great natural wonders of the world. It is the greatest barrier reef in existence, and for the interest, variety, and beauty of the life it contains it is probably unrivalled by any other region of similar extent, whether on the land or in the sea. The work of the tiny coral polyps responsible for the 1250 miles of coral, for the formation of hundreds of coral islands, is amazing enough, but the habits of much of the animal life associated with the reef are almost incredibly wonderful.

In the Great Barrier Reef nature has allowed herself to run riot. Marine animals which elsewhere are small and inconspicuous may grow there to be giants of their race; those which elsewhere are drab and unattractive may be seen there displayed in the most brilliant of colours. The colourful life of the reef is one of its greatest attractions. Whether it be the delicate tints of the corals or the brilliant hues of the fish and the clams, the beauty displayed by the reef is not surpassed by any other forms of life, not even by the flowers of our gardens. No description can adequately convey to the mind an impression of the beauty of the coral and the life associated with it, and it was a realization of this which stimulated me to obtain the natural-colour photographs that illustrate this book. These are reproduced from Lumière autochromes and are true to life in every detail. The colours the reader sees in these illustrations are the actual colours, without exaggeration, without distortion, of the objects they portray. With the exception of the slate-pencil urchin illustrated in Plate 25, fig. 2, the whole of the animal life illustrated was photographed with the objects beneath the water.

And so this book is an attempt to tell the story of the wonderful life of the reef, to give the reader an accurate impression of the colour of some of its inhabitants. Scientific terms and technicalities have been scrupulously avoided; to the layman (for whom this book is primarily intended) they make reading difficult and oftentimes obscure. No attempt has been made to include the biological nomenclature after the vernacular names of the various forms of life described, but it is hoped that the needs of the naturalist have been served by the provision of a glossary indicating the principal references.

If this book serves to stimulate in the reader an interest in the great natural wonders of the reef; if it stirs in him a desire to visit this masterpiece of nature's craftsmanship; and if, when he goes there, he is helped to understand and to appreciate the wealth, the interest, and the beauty of the life he sees, then it will have abundantly served the purpose for which it was conceived and written.

On account of the large number of illustrations throughout the book it has been found impracticable in a number of cases so to group them that they lie in close proximity to the text that refers to them. Any inconvenience which this may occasion I am sure the reader will pardon.

It is with very great pleasure indeed that I acknowledge my indebtedness to Captain Chris. Poulson, who, during my

stay at Heron Island in the winter of 1935, provided every
facility, including the construction of a photographic dark-
room (which really was dark in the most brilliant sunshine),
the collecting of specimens, the provision of boats, and in
countless ways contributed to the success of the work I had
gone there to do; and to Captain Bert Hallam, whose able
co-operation at Hayman Island in the winter of 1936 proved
of invaluable assistance during my stay there.

The literature on the Great Barrier Reef has been freely
consulted, and I wish to express my especial indebtedness
to the writings of Saville-Kent, E. J. Banfield, Dr W. D.
K. MacGillivray, Professor C. M. Yonge, F. W. Moorhouse, and to the splendid articles (by various authors) distributed throughout the pages of the *Australian Museum
Magazine*.

To the Trustees of the Australian Museum I am indebted for permission to reproduce Captain Frank Hurley's
photographs illustrating the harpooning of dugong (Plate
31, fig. 1) and the packing of pearl-shell (Plate 43, fig. 1),
for the use of the late A. R. McCulloch's photograph
of the stone-fish (Plate 21, fig. 1), and the photograph
by H. Barnes of the bees-wax model of this fish (Plate
29, fig. 1). To Miss Hilda Geissmann I am indebted
for the photograph showing the turtle laying her eggs
(Plate 14, fig. 2); to Milton Kent for that of the devil
ray (Plate 30, fig. 1), and to Dr Charles Wassell, of
Brisbane, for the loan of the photograph illustrating the
shark wounds on the neck of a Thursday Island native.

Finally, I must express my appreciation to the firm of
process engravers responsible for the preparation of
the colour blocks from my original transparencies. This
work was entrusted to Messrs Bacon and Company, of

Sydney, who have displayed a craftsmanship of a very high order in the difficult task allotted to them. The plates themselves bear eloquent testimony to the skill displayed in their preparation.

T. C. ROUGHLEY.

Sydney,
October 1936.

CONTENTS

LIST OF COLOURED PLATES

OTHER ILLUSTRATIONS

WONDERS OF THE
GREAT BARRIER REEF

CHAPTER ONE

We Journey to the Reef

BOUND for the Barrier Reef! Never shall I forget that exhilarating boat trip through Australia's "Grand Canal" when I made my first trip to the reef. I was tingling with subdued excitement, fired with keen anticipation of the natural wonders I had so often heard about palm-fringed coral islands; sheltered lagoons with water clear as crystal, sparkling, glittering in the sunlight; animal life infinite in its variety, absorbing, thrilling in its interest; coral gardens of great beauty; fishes gaudily coloured, amazingly patterned; fishing unrivalled in its productiveness; sunsets, peaceful, majestic, awe-inspiring.

One day in particular is indelibly printed on my memory. It was in the Hinchinbrook Passage. The day was still and the air cool and exhilarating; to the east of the *Canberra* as she ploughed her way north great pine-clad islands rose sheer from the water reflecting in its mirror-like surface an upside-down world; to the west dazzling white beaches lay at the foot of a dense and deep-green foliage; a mountain range towered high and hazy in the blue distance—all shimmering under a cloudless sky. It was one of those days when the cares of the world fall as a mantle from one's shoulders; when life feels good.

Leaning over the bow we watch the graceful evolutions of dolphins, their wet backs glistening as without apparent effort they playfully gambol in graceful curves, then bound

B

away a short distance quickly to return to continue the game. And as we watch the dolphins play we feel that here we have the very spirit of happiness, that *joie de vivre* which we poor humans, born into a world of strife and rumours of strife, are far too seldom able to display.

But are the lives of these beautiful creatures entirely free from care? I am afraid not. Like all marine animals they live a life that is full of peril. Somewhere, perhaps not a hundred yards away, lurks a great shark which may, without warning, without a formal declaration of war, dispute possession of a kingdom that is theirs to roam, and a bloody war is waged till one of the combatants is at the other's mercy. No mercy is ever given. And as we reflect we are reminded of a hard-dying superstition that sharks are an easy prey to dolphins, that where dolphins are sharks are never found. In a fight between a dolphin and a shark the dolphin has little chance; the skin of the shark, densely armour-plated with myriads of small teeth, offers a resistance that the dolphin's jaws would have difficulty in penetrating, while the shark's teeth, perhaps as sharp as needles, perhaps with saw-like edges, are efficient in the extreme and will tear through the dolphin's hide with ease. Many times have I found the remains of dolphins in the stomachs of sharks.

From a contemplation of the dolphins at play our gaze wanders again over the surface of the sea; there is a sudden movement to our right and our attention is riveted to a flying fish as it speeds gracefully a foot or two above the water. We saw only portion of the flight, and, our curiosity thoroughly aroused, we are on the qui vive for further exhibitions. Flying fishes are common in these waters and we have not long to wait. This time we see the fish emerge; for some distance it skims over the surface with its body at an angle of about thirty degrees, its tail in the water vibrating with great rapidity as the fish gains momentum for its flight. Suddenly it rises, its body assumes the horizontal, and with its great pectoral fins rigidly outstretched it soars through the air for a hundred, two hundred yards. Its speed has gradually decreased, and in aviation parlance it appears about to stall when, with its tail again in the water, it vigorously gathers momentum for a continuance of its flight. Another hundred yards and it ignominiously flops back into the water.

As we gaze we cannot help pondering on the extraordinary adaptation that has given rise to this fish's powers of flight; we cannot help wondering how it maintains itself in the air. For generations verbal wars have been waged on the question of the flight of the flying fish. On the one hand it has been maintained that it is capable of a soaring flight only, its pectoral fins, arched or cambered like the wings of birds or of aeroplanes, providing sufficient supporting surface and lift to enable the fish to soar after it has gained the necessary impetus from the vigorous movements of the tail as with increasing speed it skims along the surface. On the other hand some observers maintain that the flight of flying fishes is accomplished by the rapid and continual beating of the pectoral fins against the air. That it is a soaring flight is perfectly clear to a careful observer. A glance at the photograph (Plate 9, fig. 1), which I was fortunate enough to secure on this memorable day, will show that the pectoral fins are held outstretched at right angles to the body, and not pointing backwards as most drawings of the fish in flight would indicate; the ventral fins, smaller but also widely extended, obviously serve as balancing planes. Now, the muscles that control the flapping of the wings of birds are of great size and are enormously powerful, while those controlling the movements of the pectoral fins of flying fishes are far too feeble to flap them at great speed against the air.

The contention that the flying fish rapidly vibrates its outspread fins is probably the result of uncritical observations. When the fish is propelling itself forward with its tail in the water the outspread pectoral fins do vibrate rapidly, but it is a vibration conveyed to them through the vigorous lateral movements of the tail. Once the fish is free from the water the function of the tail alters from that of a propeller to that of a rudder and the pectoral fins remain rigid.

The flight of flying fishes therefore consists of a rush to the surface with both pectoral and ventral fins folded against the body; the projection of the body into the air with the caudal fin in the water (the lower lobe of the caudal fin is considerably larger than the upper); the spreading of the pectoral fins during this preliminary "taxying"; the complete emergence of the fish followed by the expansion of the ventral fins which causes the fish to assume a horizontal position; then a soaring flight of varied duration.

That so far is perfectly clear. But how has this extraordinary development come about? We are going to meet a multitude of such problems on the reef, and for the most part we can only conjecture wildly. Rarely can we supply a sufficient answer. It must never be forgotten, however, that these adaptations have taken millions of years to develop, and in our short span on earth, a mere tick in geological time, we cannot see them evolving, and experiments over such a brief interval are of little value.

There seems little doubt, however, that the flight of the flying fish has developed through the ages from efforts on the part of the fish to escape from its predatory foes. When

PLATE 1.

SUNRISE ON A CORAL ISLAND
The sun, rising over still waters, heralds a perfect day.

HERON ISLAND AT LOW TIDE
This island is typical of scores of coral islands of the Barrier Reef.

pursued by other fish, it dashes to the surface as a means of escape. An intimate description of the pursuit and escape of a flying fish, as seen from below, has been given us by William Beebe in his *Arcturus Adventure*. "Almost on the last day of my diving at Cocos," he writes, "I saw a beautiful flying fish swimming over my mushroom coral city. I had hardly registered it when the reason for its presence in this unlikely spot was explained. A long, narrow fish came up behind, slowly at first, then with a rush—a needle-toothed garfish.* The flying fish gave two or three convulsive surges forward and then I saw what I had never expected to—one of these fish rise from the water above me and disappear into the air. Somehow this made me feel more like one of the actual inhabitants of this underworld than anything which had occurred heretofore. I was seeing things from a real fish-eye view.

"The gar missed his prey and I was interested to see that he became utterly confused, and made one short rush after the other in various directions. I saw the flying fish drop into the water only twenty feet away, coming into view with a flop. The gar showed no signs of having sensed this, and the last I saw of the two, the pursued was vanishing into the blue distance while the gar turned back the way it had come."

Accurate data on the speed and the length of flight of flying fishes have not been obtained; the speed is governed to some extent by the direction and strength of the wind, but it seems probable that it averages about twenty-five miles per hour, while there is little doubt that flights of upwards of a quarter of a mile are of frequent occurrence.

Thus we spend the day, our interest divided between the kaleidoscopic beauty of the landscape around us and the dis-

* Usually called "long-tom" in Australia.

plays of the fishes and dolphins below us. We long to stay in these placid waters, to explore the bays that everywhere abound, to climb the rugged hills and admire the views that would expand beneath us, to angle in the blue depths for the fish that we know abound there; but our boat continues to throw the spray from her bows, and we must perforce continue our journey.

As dusk approaches we are attracted by a speck in the sky, and peering closely we identify a frigate-bird, a ruthless and dreaded marauder. High in the air it poises with outstretched wings, its body motionless, floating. Here we have a splendid example of true soaring. For a full half-hour a frigate-bird, facing the wind, will maintain its position without any apparent effort, without once beating its wings. Suddenly from seaward comes a gull flying leisurely after a day's foraging for small fish. It sights the frigate-bird high above it, and recognizing an uncompromising enemy it veers to the right and flies with all the power it can command; it has the responsibility of young ones to feed. But the frigate-bird has seen it and rushes down at an incredible speed. Straining every muscle of its body the gull makes a valiant effort to escape but has no chance of outstripping its enemy swooping from above. It seems inevitable that its fate is sealed. But now an extraordinary thing happens. It disgorges the fish, the product of a day's industrious quest, and the frigate-bird, with amazing adroitness, catches the fish in its beak long before they can reach the water. This sky pirate has achieved its end; it is its habit to lie in wait for gulls and other birds returning with full crops which it induces them to disgorge out of sheer fright. Some baby gulls went hungry that night.

We cannot help pitying that gull, but then we reflect that the gull itself is a notorious robber of the eggs of other birds. Moreover, it is equally a pirate and a bully when it meets a bird, such as a tern, which is smaller and weaker than itself. After the tern has had a successful day's fishing the gull will worry and harass it till it disgorges its fish and then the gull, as did the frigate-bird, will catch the fish on the wing or snatch them from the surface of the water on which they have fallen.

And so our wonderful day ends. The moon has climbed the highest hill and from the eastern summit sheds her silvery light across the sea. As we lean over the rail our thoughts roam from the strange realities of the day that has closed to conjectures on the days that are to come.

Beneath a veneer of beauty we are destined to find that life on the reef, teeming though it is with interest, is intensely cruel. Amid scenes of peacefulness that superficially seem entire, there is a lurking savagery that is relentless; although outwardly calm the war that is waged is incessant, and eternal vigilance is necessary or death follows swiftly.

The daily slaughter is prodigious. One must kill or be killed.

And because of this fierce struggle for existence we shall find on the one hand the most extraordinary weapons of offence and on the other the most subtle means of defence. It is in the contemplation of these adaptations, which on the surface would appear to indicate an amazing cunning, that we are going to find one of our most alluring interests on the reef.

CHAPTER
TWO

On a Coral Island:
First Impressions

IT is a paradox that most visitors to the Great Barrier Reef
do not see the reef at all; many of them return without
seeing a true coral island. The reason is that the majority
visit islands close to the mainland; these are usually chosen
because they are reached more quickly, and because of their
rugged charm and the scenic beauty that surrounds them.
But they are not coral islands; in past ages they formed
high hills on the coast of the mainland, which then extended
much farther east than it does to-day. This part of the
coast gradually sank beneath the waters; the level ground
and the valleys became the ocean floor, and the hills alone
remained above the surface.

These rugged islands are composed for the most part of
hard rock, such as granite, but they usually have a fringing
reef of coral and an associated fauna similar in most respects
to that which is found about a true coral island; the coral is,
however, far less prolific and the land vegetation of quite a
different character.

We must explore both, and shall first visit a coral island
in the Capricorn Group.

Leaving Gladstone, a township on the shores of Port
Curtis and on the track of the Brisbane-Cairns railway, about
ten o'clock in the morning we head for Heron Island, some
forty-five miles to the north-east. At about two o'clock
we sight our first coral island; Masthead Island looms up

as a dense clump of trees hazy in the distance; the sandy beach beneath the trees cannot yet be seen and the vegetation appears to be elevated above the surface of the water. An hour later and we pass close alongside; the tide is fairly high and we see only a dense vegetation surrounded by a snowy white beach that dazzles our eyes in the sunshine. A little later we pass Erskine Island, which looks very similar, and at about five o'clock we reach Heron Island (Plate 1, fig. 2). The tide is still high and the launch runs right in over the reef and anchors within a hundred yards of the beach. A short row in a dinghy and we step ashore on the coral sand. Comfortable huts await our coming and we quickly unpack our belongings. After a well-cooked meal we retire early, for a big day awaits us on the morrow.

We awake in the dim light before the dawn to find a perfect stillness and a cloudless sky. An auspicious day to explore the reef. Making to the beach we watch the sun, a flaming red sphere, rise seemingly out of the water, reflecting a ruddy glow which trails right to the water's edge. Donning our costumes we plunge into the shallow lagoon. The water sparkles like champagne but is far more exhilarating; we frolic and gambol like children, and our laughter is unrestrained; yesterday mundane things weighed heavily upon us, to-day we haven't a care in the world. When at last we reluctantly leave the water we feel completely refreshed, radiantly happy. For jaded nerves, for lassitude or depression, the waters of the Great Barrier Reef act as a tonic more stimulating than anything I know.

At breakfast we are introduced to some fish from the reef; this morning it is a choice between red emperor and coral trout. We like the name "red emperor" and it sways our choice; we find ourselves repeating our order for its white, flaky flesh is delicious. At this we express surprise, for we always understood that fish from colder waters were of finer flavour than those from warmer waters, but we shall soon find that the Great Barrier Reef produces fish not only of rare beauty but of a flavour and consistency unsurpassed anywhere on the Australian coast. We want to linger over our breakfast, but the tide is fast leaving the lagoon; the reef edge is already exposed, and irregular coral boulders here and there stand high above it. Clad in shorts, a shirt and sandshoes, and armed with a bucket and cold chisel, we make for the edge, about a quarter of a mile distant.

Perhaps we find our introduction to the coral life somewhat disappointing. Expecting to see brilliantly coloured coral everywhere growing luxuriantly like a garden under intense cultivation, we find that most of the highest coral in the lagoon is dead, dull, and uninteresting; but it serves to throw the living coral, which is abundant enough, into greater relief. Here in the lagoon much of the coral has grown to a height that leaves it exposed to the sun and air for long periods at low tide and consequently it has died and lost all its original beauty; the coral growing at lower levels, however, continues to thrive. Our walk takes us over patches of coral sand where the water reaches to our knees, and over the surface of coral platforms where we must tread warily lest we break through the more solid crust and, sinking, scratch our legs, for coral scratches may take a long time to heal.

Our first ramble over the reef, more in the nature of a general survey than a study of detail, is full of interest, for the life that everywhere abounds differs so greatly from anything we have ever seen before. We come across many animals of a type with which we are familiar, but we are astonished at their far greater size, their singular beauty, or their curiously specialized adaptations to a life on the reef.

We are lost in admiration for the clams, their sinuous mantle edges displaying a wealth of brilliant colours which we find words inadequate to describe (Plates 36 and 37). Rich greens, blues, purples, fawns and browns, or mottled combinations of those colours, intermingle with more sober hues; all have the appearance of the softest velvet and they abound everywhere. With the exception of the coral fishes the clams are probably the most colourful objects of the reef, at least one might say they are the most conspicuously colourful, for the tentacles of many tube worms are equally as brilliant, but they are small and are usually withdrawn into the tube at our approach. There are many other animals that vie with the clams in beauty but are seen only occasionally and usually have to be searched for. What, for instance, could be more beautiful than the naked mollusc illustrated in Plate 39?

But if the clams may be regarded as the most colourful of reef life, the anemones must always hold a high place for their delicate beauty (Plates 15, 16, 17, 22, 23). They are the flowers of the reef; many bear a close resemblance to chrysanthemums or cactus dahlias. The anemones are rarely conspicuous; apparently sensitive of the delicacy of their colours they usually hide in crevices and hollows where their tender tentacles are less susceptible to the disturbing influence of wave action.

Prominent in every pool and conspicuous for their ugliness rather than their beauty are long, drab bêche-de-mer, or sea-slugs, which have been described as great, sluggishly-animated sausages (Plate 10, fig. 1). They abound everywhere and their colours vary from pale cream through mottled browns to black; one that is particularly prevalent throughout the reef is black on the upper surface and a bright crimson below. In size they range from a few inches to about eighteen inches in length.

Also very abundant, conspicuous, and widely distributed over the whole of the lagoon are large, irregularly shaped masses which when bared by the tide lie like spineless creatures that have collapsed of their own weight. These are Alcyonarians, usually referred to as "soft" corals on account of their soft leathery or rubbery texture (Plate 12). They are closely related to the true or "hard" corals and resemble them in their minute structure, but they have not the faculty of secreting lime and therefore lack the rigid supporting skeleton characteristic of all hard corals. They vary greatly in form and some of the smaller ones are distinctly beautiful, though many of the larger ones repel rather than attract; indeed, some of them resemble giant warty or cancerous outgrowths on the reef. The commonest forms are usually green, yellow, or brown in colour; the expansive surface is finely pitted and leathery with the edges folded, convoluted, or produced into finger-like processes. The visitor sees them, however, only in the daytime when the animal is quiescent, but at night their surface is covered with extended polyps each bearing eight feathery tentacles that serve to catch their food, and then the whole aspect of the animal is changed. Under these conditions most of the soft corals are distinctly beautiful.

Seaweeds grow in profusion everywhere; some are as soft as down, others coarse and brittle; their colours range from a bright, rich green, through various shades of brown to a deep red. They form a welcome contrast to the dominating hard coral and provide a delightful setting for many forms of animal life that favour their environment.

We find the reef edge to be a solid platform, hard and unyielding, for the most part elevated and flat. Most of

PLATE 2.

GOLDEN SANDS
In the light of the setting sun the coral-sand turns to gold.

A CORAL POOL

the coral is alive but stunted in its growth (Plate 6, figs
1 and 2); the colours are variable, though browns predominate. Scattered almost everywhere are large coral
boulders, which are referred to usually as nigger-heads
(Plate 44, fig. 2); these, it is generally agreed, have
been dislodged from the deeper water during very heavy
seas and have been deposited high on the edge of the reef.
The coral throughout the whole length of the reef edge,
which extends for many miles and encloses a huge lagoon on
the eastern side of the island, remains everywhere dwarfed,
partly on account of its elevation, partly on account of the
swiftly-running water that passes over it at every ebb and
flow of the tide.

The flat surface of the reef edge is broken everywhere
by coral pools, some small, a foot or two in diameter and
a few inches deep, others with a diameter of many yards
and a depth up to ten or twelve feet. On the sides of these
pools coral of many forms and hues grows in profusion,
while the bottom is usually composed of sand or sandy-
coloured coral rock. Lying motionless on the bottom,
bêche-de-mer are to be seen in almost every pool, and fishes
of amazing patterns and vivid colours swim lazily in the
crystal water.

On the seaward edge of the reef corals of the more hardy
forms thrive. This edge is constantly battered by the break
of the surf and the more delicate kinds cannot long survive.
The dominant type is that which forms a series of ledges or
platforms with a circular outline.

Such are the first impressions gained by a stroll through
the coral gardens of the lagoon and an examination of the
reef edge. But we must be making back for the tide is
already beginning to flow into the lagoon and our passage
will be difficult if the coral is covered with water.

The following day we decide to explore the deeper water beyond the reef and requisition a glass-bottomed boat for the purpose.

Although it is July, and midwinter, the cloudless sky provides a comfortable warmth as we lazily paddle our boat over the mirror-like surface beyond the reef where the water is twenty or thirty feet deep. Here the coral, never exposed to the retarding influence of the air, never battered by waves churned up by an angry wind, is free to grow in almost limitless profusion and it reaches a size never attained in the shallow water of the lagoon. As we gaze into the cool green light of the liquid depths we are transported into a new world, and we fairly gasp with wonder at the magnificence of the scene below us. Here are coral gardens that might have been planted and tended by fairies, so strangely different are they from the gardens of our previous experience. Delicate, finely branched coral trees and shrubs, corals like giant mushrooms, corals resembling enormous fans, corals arranged in tiers like a Buddhist temple, coral grottoes, coral caves, corals infinite in their variety, pass by as we slowly and quietly move over the surface. Their colours are restful rather than brilliant. A hedge of light blue staghorn coral contrasts with one of pink; branches of lavender are thrown into relief by borders of rose red. Here and there the coral shrubs are variegated; pale green stems are tipped with mauve, like buds about to burst into bloom; bright yellow branches tipped with pale blue; pale fawn tipped with heliotrope. The shape and colour are limitless.

We cannot help feeling resentment that we must remain in a world apart; that we cannot live our lives in the peaceful atmosphere of this garden of our dreams. We cannot help envying the multitude of fishes whose good fortune

it is to make these gardens their permanent abode. Wherever we look fishes, unaware of, or at least undisturbed by,
our presence, swim lazily about the maze of coral growth,
apparently proud of the beauty that surrounds them. Or is
it pride in their own beauty? They at least have every
reason to be proud, for nature has adorned them with lavish
prodigality. Their colours are indescribable—they live;
and their shapes and patterns beggar description. Small
demoiselles, three or four inches long, adorned with a blue
of wonderful purity, some with golden tails, vie with
others of a uniform green shade rare in the world above.
The colourful patterns of stripes and spots which many of
these coral fishes display cause us to wonder whether our
eyes are not playing us some strange trick. But not all the
fish are small. We pass over many which anglers continually tempt with their lures and feel that angling in this
world of peace and beauty is sacrilege indeed. Here we
see coral cod (Plate 47, fig. 1), brilliant scarlet inlaid
with fine blue spots; king snapper (Plate 47, fig. 2) of
a pearly lustre with red bands in the shape of a broad arrow;
red-mouthed emperor (Plate 48, fig. 2), iridescent silvery blue with blood-red markings on the fins and body;
parrot-fishes adorned with the coat of Joseph; and many
others equally beautiful.

Suddenly the peace of this happy community is disturbed;
the fish dash in confusion to the shelter of the nearest coral,
and almost in an instant the whole population has disappeared. Intent on the beauty beneath us we have failed to
notice the approach of a huge shark which, silent and sinis-
ter, has slowly moved into this world of peace, seeking
whom it may devour. It seems all wrong that such cruel
marauders should be allowed entry into paradise.

We return from our tour of the submerged coral gardens

filled with an intense satisfaction, feeling that we have come to earth from another world, a strange world entirely different from that to which we belong, and we wonder whether it can all be true.

And now for the island itself. Heron Island is typical of scores of coral islands throughout the Great Barrier Reef. Differences occur in size and shape, in the extent and disposition of the reefs that border them, and to some extent in their vegetation, but superficially there is a striking similarity. Their size is governed mainly by their age, beginning from the time when they first began to project as growing coral above the surface of the water; their shape, usually roughly oval, is determined largely by the strength and duration of the prevailing winds; their vegetation by the forms of plant life that were first to gain a foothold in the early days of the island's existence.

Heron Island is a coral cay, so called to distinguish it from a coral atoll, which forms a more or less complete ring of coral and coral sand exposed to the air at high tide and therefore permanently enclosing a lagoon. A cay is a coral island that has no central lagoon; it is usually more or less surrounded by a coral rampart which may be many miles in extent and in the form of a great oval, with the island situated near one of the narrow extremities. This rampart is somewhat more elevated than the area between it and the island; it is exposed to the air at low tide and encloses a large expanse of water which is frequently referred to as a "lagoon," but it is not strictly a lagoon, for at high tide the enclosing rampart is completely submerged. If, therefore, the term "lagoon" is used here for this body of water it is only because it appears as such when the tide is low and is therefore usually referred to as a lagoon by those who wander over it at low tide.

PLATE 3.

CORAL EXPOSED DURING A LOW SPRING TIDE

Heron Island is about a mile in circumference; it is every-where surrounded by a beach of coral sand which circum-scribes a dense vegetation. The principal trees are Pisonias (Plate 46), which grow to a height of about sixty feet, with mottled grey trunks that may be several feet in diameter at the base. Their timber is soft and brittle, and if one climbs them great care must be exercised, for boughs of considerable thickness are likely to crash without warning beneath one's weight. The foliage is a delightful soft green reminiscent of the green of European rather than Australian trees. An occasional Tournefortia-tree, much smaller and with silvery green lustrous foliage; clumps of Pandanus-trees with their tufted leaves and stilt-like roots (Plate 41); and Casua-rinas or beach-oaks, which in many places border the forest externally, complete the more massive vegetation of the island, while shrubs of various kinds are in places so dense that a passage through them is almost impossible. A coarse grass grows on the higher limits of the beach tending every-where to bind it.

The whole island is composed of coral sand except in the intertidal zone along the southern shore; here coarse coral rock forms a more or less continuous border. The highest part of the island is probably not more than about fifteen feet above high-water level.

This type of vegetation covers, with slight variations, all the islands of the Capricorn Group, but, although all of them are heavily vegetated, the dominant types of trees vary greatly. For instance, Wilson Island, distant from Heron Island only about eight miles, is densely covered with Pan-danus-trees (Plate 50, fig. 1) which almost everywhere form an impenetrable jungle, their maze of prop-like roots giving them a grotesquely weird appearance. So crowded are they that every other form of plant life has been choked out

c

beneath them and their dead and fallen leaves form a soft carpet, in many places a foot or more deep. The island is fringed here and there by Pisonias, Tournefortias, and Casuarinas.

On North Reef, where a lighthouse guides shipping into the southern end of the Grand Canal through the Capricorn Channel, Tournefortias occur in greatest abundance; the low trees are so dense that they form in places an unbroken hedge, while other forms of vegetation are sparsely distributed. This island boasts a magnificent Pandanus-tree whose dome-shaped foliage extends right to the ground.

Farther north many of the islands bear coco-nut palms which lend an atmosphere of tropical beauty. Here, also, where the reef is much closer to the mainland, muddy areas occur round some of the islands, and mangroves of several species are found in abundance.

In striking contrast to these low-lying islands of coral sand, the mainland islands are rocky, rugged, and elevated. Most of them are uninhabited, but, on some, tourists are catered for, and their proximity to the mainland, coupled with the fact that passengers may be disembarked adjacent to several of them from steamers proceeding north from Brisbane, has rendered them very popular. Chief of the tourist islands are Lindeman and Brampton in the Cumberland Group; Hayman, West Molle, South Molle (also called Daydream Island) and Long Island in the Whitsunday Group; and Dunk Island (immortalized by Banfield) north of the Hinchinbrook Group.

The shores of these islands are in most places very rugged, interrupted here and there by beautiful white beaches. Great granite rocks, rising hundreds of feet sheer from the water, form ever-present reminders of some violent upheaval of the past when these areas were part of the mainland. The vegetation is that of the mainland and although, if a census were taken, eucalypts would probably be found to predominate, the great hoop pine forests are much more striking and conspicuous. But many other trees and shrubs occur in great profusion. Tournefortias, beach-oaks, Pandanus-trees and an occasional coco-nut palm fringe many of the beaches, while umbrella-trees, wattles, tea-trees, native plums (conspicuous in the winter by their oval fruits of deep scarlet about two and a half inches long), and a host of others cover the low-lying areas, and ferns and orchids are plentifully distributed through the gullies.

Many of the islands have fringing coral reefs which, although never so extensive as those of the Barrier Reef, nevertheless display coral of great beauty and variety, while clams and other shellfish, bêche-de-mer, crabs, starfish, and the other forms of life associated with coral may be very abundant.

Then, of course, their scenic beauty forms one of their greatest attractions. From their elevated hills can be seen vast areas of sea studded with islands, some small and comparatively low-lying, others many miles in extent, their peaks frequently enveloped in clouds.

The reader contemplating a trip to the Barrier Reef will obtain all the information he requires concerning travelling facilities and accommodation from the Queensland Government Tourist Bureau in Brisbane, or its branches in the capital cities of the other States.

CHAPTER	*Twelve Hundred*
THREE	*Miles of Coral*

THE Great Barrier Reef of Australia is the greatest coral reef in the world. It is approximately 1250 miles long and encloses an area of about 80,000 square miles consisting of an intricate maze of coral reefs, islets, and shoals, much of it uncharted. The distance of its outer edge from the coast varies from about ten to one hundred and fifty miles and averages probably from twenty to thirty miles. On the north it reaches almost to the New Guinea coast and on the south as far as Breaksea Spit, a little north of Sandy Cape; or at least those are the northern and southern limits of the area of reef-building coral. Strictly speaking the barrier portion of the reef may be said to terminate on the south at Swain Reefs; between these and Breaksea Spit it is represented by a scattered series of reefs and coral islands. The most southern coral island is Lady Elliot Island, which is about half a mile in circumference and is surmounted by a lighthouse. A little to the north a series of three small coral islets form the Bunker Group, and these are followed by a number of islands scattered round the tropic of Capricorn from which they have received the name of the Capricorn Group. The northernmost of the Capricorns is North Reef, a small sandy island with a lighthouse that guides shipping into the Capricorn Channel separating North Reef from Swain Reefs. This channel, which is about sixty miles wide, gradually shelves from about seventy to thirty

PLATE 4.

A PARTY ON THE REEF
Clad in colourful bathing costumes, these tourists discuss a rare find.

VARIEGATED BRANCHING CORAL ON WISTARI REEF

fathoms, and is much deeper than the boat channel border-ing the coast, which averages about twenty fathoms. Ships leaving Brisbane pass north outside the coral islands lying south of North Reef, and entering the Capricorn Channel make north-west towards the coast of the mainland, which they skirt till they reach Cape York. This boat passage inside the reef has received the name of Australia's "Grand Canal."

Swain Reefs form an intricate maze of coral, most of which is uncharted. Their outer edge is about one hundred and fifty miles from the mainland and they are about forty or fifty miles wide. From their northern extremity a chain of reefs extends north-west; they are at first very discon-nected; the channels separating them are fairly wide and comparatively frequent, but as the reef extends north into warmer waters the length of the individual reefs becomes much greater and the channels fewer, till in the northern area of the reef dividing channels are very rare. Gradu-ally the reef approaches closer to the coast; opposite Towns-ville the outer edge is only fifty miles away; opposite Cairns it is within twenty miles, and still farther north, to the east of Cape Melville, it is but ten miles distant. North of Cape Melville the reef continues parallel with the coast for about a hundred and fifty miles and then sheers off to run due north while the coast extends towards the north-west. As a result of this divergence it encloses an increasing body of water and east of Cape York it is about eighty miles from the coast.

North of Cape York the Barrier becomes more irregular and disjointed till it loses its identity as a barrier to the south of Flinders Passage, or north-east of Murray Islands. From Flinders Passage it forms an irregular mass of broken reefs extending almost to the New Guinea coast.

The western limit of the Great Barrier Reef area lies about north of the western shore of Cape York Peninsula, the approximate boundary extending along a group of Torres Strait islands of considerable elevation, including Prince of Wales, Thursday, and Badu islands, with many intervening shoals and reefs. The reef area lying between the eastern and western limits in Torres Strait resembles that farther south between the outer barrier and the mainland; it embraces an intricate mass of reefs separated by irregularly winding channels.

It is clear, therefore, that this great reef is not a complete barrier; on its northern aspect its continuity is rarely broken, but the gaps increase as it extends south, culminating in the very wide Capricorn Channel, to the south of which the reefs and islands are scattered about almost indiscriminately.

For the most part the individual reefs comprising this outer barrier are submerged at high tide; many of them are never bared by the tide at all, but they do form a very effective barrier or rampart against the ocean swell. For hundreds of miles along its northern extent a south-east trade-wind blows consistently for about nine months of the year and the heavy sea it brings in its train pounds the outer edge of the reef, but there its force is dissipated and the water within remains comparatively calm, a short, choppy sea being the limit to which the wind can stir it.

Cruising inside the Barrier we see a long line of savage surf foaming white as it relentlessly thunders on the coral edge to spend itself as it broils over the reef crest; it is a magnificent spectacle, rendered weird and wonderful be- cause its fury has no apparent cause. But though the en- closed sea is smooth it is by no means plain sailing. From the outer edge of the Barrier almost to the mainland, coral reefs and islands form an intricate maze from Cape York to the Capricorns, and navigation in anything but small craft is impossible. Submerged coral reefs abound everywhere and the channels that divide them are navigable only by boatmen with long experience in those waters.

Fortunately the scattered reefs do not extend to the coast, otherwise a journey north in a liner would be impossible. Another barrier consisting of innumerable rocky islands forms their western boundary and between these islands and the mainland a safe passage for shipping remains. These islands, as we have seen, are mainland islands; they are the peaks of what was once a mountain range along the eastern Queensland coast, but owing to the sinking of the land the surrounding areas have become submerged. As we journey north along the Queensland coast these islands are rarely out of sight; they form a chain almost as continuous as the reefs of the outer barrier, but whereas the latter are every-where low-lying, frequently submerged, the former are for the most part high, rugged, and extremely picturesque. The water they enclose resembles a succession of fiords. Their size and height vary greatly; in the Whitsunday Passage some are several miles long and may rise to a height of nearly 1500 feet; in the Hinchinbrook Passage they are even larger and grander. The lofty peaks of wild, mys-terious Hinchinbrook Island rise to a height of over 3000 feet, and the island itself is nearly thirty miles long. Most of these mainland islands are bordered by fringing reefs of varying extent, and they are favourite resorts of tourists.

And now we must consider how this enormous extent of coral has come about. What has determined its present disposition? Why has it not extended farther south to the New South Wales coast? How have the coral islands been formed?

Up to the present we have been concerned with hard

facts, with coral islands, submerged reefs and channels, and great lofty islands jutting sheer from the water. These we can see and explore and investigate. But when we come to an explanation of the why and the wherefore of their existence we are dealing with something far less tangible; we are endeavouring to peer into the remote past extending back thousands, perhaps millions, of years. We enter the realm of speculation, of theory. To gain an insight into these questions we study the facts as presented by the disposition and the growth of the coral as we find it to-day; we endeavour to determine the conditions that govern its growth and we apply to all the evidence so gathered the knowledge gained by a study of geology and geography in their many spheres.

But still we cannot be certain. Several theories have been advanced to account for the formation and disposition of the Great Barrier Reef, but a critical examination of these is not intended here. We shall content ourselves with a brief discussion of that which is most generally accepted by modern scientific opinion.

In order to understand the problem we shall have to travel a considerable way back in geological time. In some past age the Queensland coast extended farther east than it does to-day; not very much farther in the north but considerably farther in the south. This area consisted of flat or undulating country with a range of hills and lofty peaks a few miles to the east of the present coastline. Gradually this area, due possibly to the cooling of the earth's surface, began to subside; as it sank the sea swept over it killing all the vegetation that previously covered it. It formed the bottom of a shallow sea, and as we have already noted, the tops of the highest hills projected above the level of the water as islands.

Now, the shallow depth and the warm water favoured the growth of reef-building corals. They became established and naturally flourished most in situations where conditions were most favourable. This growth was retarded by the influence of fresh water and by sediment poured into this shallow sea by rivers that flowed into its western boundary, and so the coral flourished best on the eastern side of the shallow ledge where the water was clearer and purer.

In view of the retarding influence of fresh water it might be expected that the growth of coral would be more abundant on the south where the edge of the shallow sea was farthest from the coast, but here intervenes another factor which has a great determining influence on the growth of coral, that of temperature. The water in these southern regions is not so warm as that in the north and it tends to slow down the growth of the coral. There appears to be little doubt that, if the temperature of the water in the southern area of the reef were as high as in the north the growth of coral in the region of the Tropic of Capricorn, where the ledge extends about a hundred and fifty miles east of the present coastline, would be far more prolific at its outer edge than on any part of the Great Barrier Reef.

And so the coral began its long task of building the outer barrier. Under any conditions it was a gigantic task, but it was probably rendered far greater by a continuance of the floor of the sea to subside, and it therefore developed into the nature of a race between the two—the corals ever building upwards and the floor beneath them sinking. The corals won, but paradoxically they succeeded largely because of many agencies that tended to destroy them. As they grew upward towards the sun the older, lower portions died; they were perhaps choked by growths of seaweed on their surface or killed by a horde of animals that bored into their skeletons for protection. Gradually they crumbled and disintegrated into coral sand. As the destruction continued the level of this sand imperceptibly but surely rose; the coral it supported continued to flourish and to die; and through the ages it grew nearer and nearer to the surface.

At last the coral reached the air, and the sand that supported it crept up beneath it till it, too, became exposed, and a coral island was born. On every side its extent was increased, birds rested on it and their droppings helped to store up nutriment for plant life that might be destined to reach this little island. Some of these birds perhaps carried the seeds of grass, or of shrubs, or of trees even, attached to their feet or feathers, or perhaps seeds, impervious for long periods to the action of sea-water, were washed ashore and left high and dry. They germinated; their roots found sufficient nourishment in the sand; the grass bound the sand and stabilized it; and so this little coral island became vegetated.

Most of the reefs still remain below the surface of the water, but they continue to rise and if the weather conditions that obtain to-day persist long enough, and if the sea floor does not sink at a rate faster than the corals can grow, it appears inevitable that the Great Barrier Reef, or that part of it which forms the outer barrier, will in ages to come form a long, continuous island.

There was another important agency assisting in this process of building. Besides the elevation caused by the disintegration of the coral into sand there was always another very potent force at work. Lime was deposited between the fragments of coral, between the shells and the calcareous carcasses of myriads of other forms of life, continually and effectively cementing them together and forming great expanses of coral rock, well able to withstand the ocean's fury. Thus a mighty rampart grew.

The growth of coral was not confined to the outer edge of the coral sea; it was most active there, but it proceeded apace over most of the area between the edge and the mainland, giving rise to countless reefs and islands. Even on the foreshores of the mainland reef-building coral occurs in situations where the conditions for its existence are favourable.

But why did the coral confine its growth to the shallow water over the submerged continental shelf? Why did it not flourish in the deeper water beyond? For the most part this is a question of the strength of the light that reaches the coral. Reef-building corals cannot grow at a depth greater than about thirty fathoms, and the water between the barrier and the mainland rarely exceeds that depth; for the most part it is far shallower. Beyond the outer edge, however, the bottom dips steeply to a depth of hundreds and in places thousands of fathoms. Now, the intensity of light falls rapidly as it penetrates the water, and below about thirty fathoms it is insufficient to maintain the minute plant life which we shall shortly see is embedded in the tissues of reef-building corals and which appears to be necessary for their existence.

The southern boundary of the reef is determined by the temperature of the water. Although corals of various forms are found on the coast of New South Wales, and are, indeed, widely distributed throughout the temperate seas of the world, a few species penetrating even into Arctic and Antarctic waters, they are of a solitary or isolated type, for the reef-building corals will not thrive in water where the temperature falls much below 68°F.

This, then, is the prevailing opinion of most present-day

scientists concerning the formation of the Great Barrier
Reef, shorn of all complications of which there are not a
few. But what of the organisms that have accomplished
this stupendous task? What is their nature? How do they
form coral; how do they multiply and spread; what do they
feed on? We shall proceed to discuss these questions in
the next chapter.

PLATE 5.

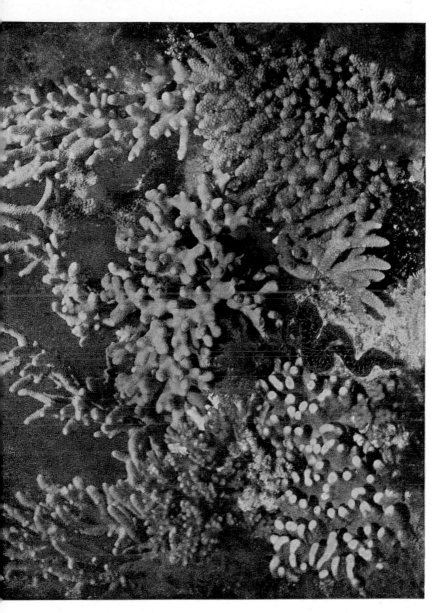

A CORAL GRCTTO

*The Nature
of Coral*

FEW people have the opportunity of seeing living coral. Their knowledge of coral is confined to the specimens they see in Museums or in the display windows of shops and Tourist Bureaux. These are merely bleached skeletons. Occasionally they are tinted to simulate the colour of the living coral, but the colours are usually crude and garish; they can never convey the soft beauty of the live coral.

These coral skeletons are composed principally of carbonate of lime, and a close examination of their surface reveals a great number of small cup-shaped pits or depressions. When the coral was alive each of these formed the home of a tiny coral polyp which was responsible for its formation by the deposition of the lime; the coral we are examining is therefore not the skeleton of one animal but the combined skeletons of hundreds, perhaps thousands, of similar animals.

Tiny polyps, then, each for the most part smaller than the head of a pin, each an industrious little architect, are responsible for the construction of these beautiful corals with a sculpture almost infinite in its variety. Their combined efforts have created the 1250 miles of coral comprising the Great Barrier Reef.

If we examine one of these cup-shaped depressions with a lens we find it is divided into vertical chambers by numerous fine plates or septa that extend from the inner surface towards the middle line; but they do not meet there; if they were cut across horizontally and looked at from above they would resemble the spokes of a wheel with the axle removed. When the polyp was alive it consisted simply of a covering of soft tissue round this limy skeleton. The mouth was situated in the centre of the free end; it was surrounded by tentacles that served to catch the food, and the stomach was simply the cavity in its interior. It also possessed fleshy partitions or mesenteries between the limy plates, and in these the germ cells developed when it was ready to breed. During the breeding-season we should find these mesenteries swollen, with masses of minute cells congregated in two different zones, one towards the outer edge which gives rise to spermatozoa, the other towards their base which develops into eggs. When fully developed the spermatozoa are liberated into the water through the mouth which is, of course, the only external aperture the animal possesses; the eggs, however, are not extruded at the same time. During the ordinary course of feeding the water is continually being drawn into the stomach cavity of the polyp and the spermatozoa are in this way received from the polyps of other corals.

The eggs remain within the parent for some time after they are fertilized, and when at length they are expelled by the muscular contractions of the walls of the polyp they are in the form of small, pear-shaped planulae covered with minute hairs which by their rapid vibration enable the embryo to swim about; they can only swim feebly, however, and they are at the mercy of tides and currents. Within a short time an indentation appears at the broader end; this gradually deepens till the embryo assumes the form of a cup when it is ready to settle down to a sedentary life after a free-swimming existence that extended over possibly a week. At this stage it must locate some hard object suitable for its attachment or perish. Having encountered such an object the embryo attaches itself by secreting a cementing liquid at the narrower end which at once broadens into a disk-shaped base, and it is then in the form of a vase standing erect. Tentacles now develop at the rim of the free extremity. Immediately after attachment this soft-bodied polyp begins to construct its skeleton by the secretion of lime.

The subsequent growth of this coral polyp to form a colony is determined by the type of coral to which it belongs. If it is a branching form, such as that known commonly as staghorn coral, it continues to grow upwards and to bud off smaller ones from the side; these grow and bud in an exactly similar manner and so give rise to the many branches characteristic of that form of coral. If the newly attached polyp is one of the more solid forms, however, it divides down the middle to form two polyps and these grow upwards together; continued divisions of this character give rise to a multitude of parallel channels which progressively form the homes of the polyps in their upward growth. In most cases as the polyp extends its tube upwards it regularly secretes a partition across it, so that instead of being a hollow tube it is divided into chambers by a series of partitions.

Each type of solid coral has its own peculiarity of structure, which produces the extremely diverse patterns seen everywhere on a coral reef.

Coral polyps gather their food usually by means of their tentacles, which are expanded at night for that purpose; during the day they lie contracted within the polyp. But even if they were expanded in the daytime they would find little food available, for the organisms on which the corals feed descend in the daytime and are found in the surface waters only at night.

Corals subsist entirely upon animal food; they cannot digest plant life. The food consists of a wide range of minute animals, with crustaceans predominating, and the size of the organisms that can be utilized is dependent on the capacity of the coral polyp to cope with them. The larger ones with prominent tentacles can, of course, handle larger organisms than the smaller ones.

The method of catching the prey is very interesting. They shoot it with poison darts. Each tentacle is provided with a large number of oval cells each of which contains a coiled, barbed spring suspended in a poisonous fluid. Instantly the tentacle is touched a host of these barbed darts shoot out, penetrate the animal and immediately paralyse it; the tentacles then bend over and convey it to the mouth, which in turn passes it into the stomach. On its arrival there the mesenteries lying between the hard septa fold over it and by their secretion of digestive juices extract the nourishment which then passes into their tissues. Digestion is very rapid; within a few hours the whole of the food material is extracted and the undigested portion is passed to the exterior through the mouth.

While this method of feeding is common to most of the corals of the Great Barrier Reef there are a few species that do not gather their food by means of tentacles but pass it to the centrally situated mouth by the vigorous beating of minute hairs or cilia.

Like all other forms of animal life corals must breathe, and they obtain the oxygen they require from the sea-water that constantly bathes them. They are not provided with any special apparatus for this purpose; the oxygen passes

PLATE 6.

GREEN ENCRUSTING CORAL ON THE CREST OF A REEF

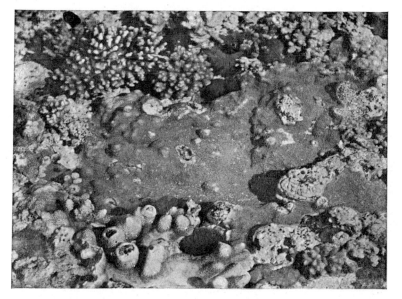

A PATCH OF CORAL BARED BY A LOW SPRING TIDE

into the animal through the thin wall of the polyp exposed to the water.

Reef-building corals have an accessory means of obtaining oxygen. They cultivate a garden in their tissues. The reader is aware, of course, that when animals breathe they absorb oxygen and give off carbon dioxide, and that plants reverse this process; they absorb carbon dioxide and give off oxygen. Obviously, if one can live in intimate association with the other it is greatly to the advantage of both. Now, plant life in the form of extremely small, single-celled Algae live in the tissues of reef-building coral with benefit both to themselves and to the coral. Each coral polyp contains thousands of these microscopic plants which thrive there; their greatest requirement is light, for only in a bright light can they live and grow, and the dependence of the coral on them for adequate supplies of oxygen restricts the growth of the coral to a comparatively shallow depth where the light is sufficiently bright to maintain them. During the daytime, therefore, the plants in the coral's tissues are actively carrying on the vital processes necessary for their existence; they are absorbing the carbon dioxide that is being produced as a waste product by the polyp, and they are producing oxygen that is immediately absorbed into the tissues of the coral. The plants convert the carbon dioxide into starch.

A most interesting and enlightening experiment that provided a striking illustration of the amount of oxygen produced by the plants embedded in the tissues of coral was carried out by the British Barrier Reef Expedition during the course of its twelve months' stay at Low Island. A coral was placed in a jar filled with water and containing a known amount of oxygen in the daytime when it was exposed to a bright light. The jar was carefully sealed and

D

when, after some hours, the oxygen content of the water was determined it was actually found to have increased. The plants in the coral produced more than the coral required. A similar experiment carried out at night had quite a different result. In the absence of light the plants were unable to produce oxygen and then the oxygen contained in the water had to be continually drawn upon and it decreased at the rate one would expect to find if the plants were not present.

One is led to conjecture how this association (which, by the way, occurs also in a number of other forms of animal life) has come about. The reason is not known with certainty but it is thought possible that on account of the extreme abundance and crowding together of corals on a reef, the amount of oxygen dissolved in the sea-water that circulates over them may be insufficient to satisfy their requirements, hence the provision of the supplementary supply in this extraordinary manner.

THE species of corals found on the Great Barrief Reef
amount to several hundreds. On account of the great
variation which many of them are subject to they are extremely difficult to classify; for instance, a certain coral
in a sheltered situation may occur as a much branched form,
but the same species growing where it is exposed to the
wash of broken water may assume the form of an encrusting growth with stunted nodules on its upper surface.

In addition to this great variation in the individual species
there is another feature of coral life which renders their
identification confusing to the layman. We have seen that
all corals are made up of polyps which lie snug in little
cup-shaped chambers of their own construction. Now, these
polyps have considerable powers of contraction and expansion; they usually withdraw completely into their homes
during the daytime, the mouths of the depressions then
alone showing at the surface, and at night they emerge
beyond the mouths of the cups and expand their tentacles
to the fullest extent. The difference in the appearance of
a coral under these conditions is very striking; with the
polyps expanded it may resemble a miniature garden, its
surface completely covered with minute, symmetrical star-
like flowers coloured perhaps a uniform green, blue, or
yellow, but when the polyps are withdrawn the appearance
of the surface is greatly altered; it may consist of a series

of ridges and depressions, maze-like and convoluted, or it may perhaps be folded, pitted, or sculptured into a confusing variety of patterns. Moreover, its colour in this condition may be entirely different from that of the expanded polyps.

On this account, therefore, it is practically impossible clearly to describe the many varieties, and even if it were attempted the reader would probably not gain much enlightenment. With few exceptions, therefore, a general indication only of the form of the most important groups will be given.

The dominating types of stony corals on the Great Barrier Reef may be divided into the slender, more fragile branching forms such as the staghorn corals, and the more solid, denser, and harder types, such as the meandrine or brain corals.

Without doubt the most conspicuous, the most universally distributed of the corals over the whole area of the Great Barrier Reef, are the staghorn corals. These have received their name from the antler-like disposition of the branches common to many species; their irregularly branching growths are usually tree-like in arrangement, while some form symmetrical shrub-like clumps. They abound over the reef flats everywhere but they reach their greatest development in sheltered situations where they are never bared by the tide.

The colours of the staghorns are among the most beautiful of all corals. A whole colony may be a uniform hue, perhaps blue, heliotrope, lavender, purple, red, pink, green, brown, yellow, and an infinite variety of intermediate shades, or the tips of the branches may assume an entirely different colour to form a pleasing and beautiful contrast. The branches may be a bright green with lilac tips; pale

PLATE 7.

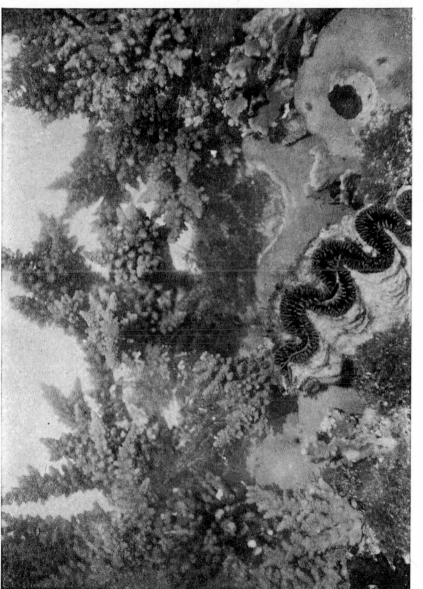

BRANCHING CORAL, LIKE TREES IN BLOSSOM, GROWING ABOVE THE MORE SOLID PORITES

In the foreground an open clam displays its beautiful blue mantle edges.

yellow with rose pink tips; light buff with pale blue tips; straw-coloured with heliotrope tips; bright pink with lemon yellow tips; and a wide range of similar combinations.

On account of their fragile nature the staghorn corals suffer great damage during heavy gales, and, in the northern area of the reef particularly, their dead and decaying branches may be seen piled up on the weather side of many islands to a depth of several feet and a width of several yards, forming a rampart hundreds of yards long.

Of an entirely different appearance are the more solid corals of which the brain coral illustrated at the bottom of Plate 40 is a typical example. These corals are usually rounded in outline, and many growing in permanently submerged situations several fathoms deep may occur as great boulders up to ten or twelve feet in diameter. The surface of these corals when the polyps are retracted may be comparatively smooth and indented with pit-like depressions, or it may be raised into a great variety of ridges, convoluted and twisted, to form highly decorative patterns. In colour, browns predominate, though combinations of bright greens and browns are very common. The brain corals, common and widely distributed throughout the whole reef area, are patterned with an extraordinary resemblance to the convolutions of the human brain.

Of even a denser and harder structure are the corals known as Porites which are scattered over nearly every reef. If allowed to grow unrestricted they are usually dome-shaped, but on reef flats and in lagoons where they are bared by the tide the upper surface dies and erodes, the coral then assuming the form of a great rounded platform or basin, the edges alone remaining alive and colourful. Subsequent growth consists of a lateral expansion which continually increases the diameter of the coral. It is not uncommon to find similar smaller corals growing out from the dead flat area; these also expand laterally until eventually the large parent coral may support several layers of similar corals above it, each of smaller diameter than that beneath it.

These Porites may attain a diameter of upwards of twenty feet with a similar height. The colour of the growing edge is frequently a beautiful lavender; the tentacles are usually similarly coloured though their expanded tips are commonly greenish-grey.

Conspicuous not so much because of its bulk, for it never grows much bigger than a dinner-plate, but because it is solitary and symmetrically patterned with thin plates radiating from the circumference towards the middle line, is the mushroom coral (lower right-hand corner of frontispiece) which lies loose on the bottom in situations where it is not disturbed by wave action. This coral, rounded or oval in outline, is flattened on its under surface while the upper surface is slightly rounded or convex; the radiating plates bear a resemblance to the "gills" of a mushroom and this has been responsible for the name commonly bestowed upon it.

While the branching forms and the more solid types we have been considering occur in colonies or communities, which may comprise in the one unit hundreds, perhaps thousands, of individual coral polyps, the mushroom coral is one large individual; it houses one polyp only, and the radiating plates or septa correspond exactly with those of its smaller relatives, which can usually be made out only with the aid of a lens.

The tentacles of some species of mushroom corals are thick and massive and when fully expanded may extend two or three inches beyond the margin of the coral; in most of the common species, however, they are relatively small and inconspicuous. In colour they range from various shades of green to brown; these are also the dominant colours of the corals when the tentacles are retracted.

Although mushroom corals breed in the usual manner by the production of eggs and spermatozoa, they have another method of reproduction which is highly interesting. In the young stage they grow upwards on stalks like mushrooms but with the radiating plates on the upper surface. When they are from an inch to an inch and a half in diameter the expanded disk breaks free and falls to the bottom, and another disk begins development at the end of the stalk.

We now come to a group of corals which, although closely related to the hard or stony corals just described, exhibit such structural modifications that they have been set apart in a class known as Alcyonaria. With few exceptions the members of this class have not the faculty of secreting lime except in the form of microscopic spicules and hence they are generally referred to as "soft" corals (Plate 12). By means of this physical characteristic alone nearly all Alcyonarians can at a glance be distinguished from their harder relatives, but there is another, an infallible method of recognizing them, that is by their tentacles; the polyps of all Alcyonarian corals bear eight tentacles, which are with rare exceptions either fringed or feather-like.

Soft corals are extremely abundant over the whole area of the Great Barrier Reef; indeed, on some reefs exposed by the tide they completely dominate all other forms of life, and by growing over the hard coral in dense masses may smother it. Some species are small and much branched; the form and colour of these may be distinctly pleasing, but the larger ones, which may attain a diameter of several feet, or yards in some cases, are for the most part ugly and repulsive; their texture is leathery and they are slimy to the touch.

The colours vary from a pale bluish-grey to red, but greens and browns of various shades predominate. Most of them are attached to coral or coral rock by a thick fleshy stalk that always remains short; it expands into a disk that rests in folds on the bottom or on the coral and other life about it. In its young stage it is more erect like a mushroom, but as the disk grows its edge becomes irregularly lobed and convoluted till on further expansion the lobes may overlap one another. The surface is everywhere covered with fine pit-shaped depressions that house the polyps; when the coral is feeding and the tentacles are expanded the whole aspect of the animal is changed; although the general shape is not obscured the flower-like tentacles give the whole surface the appearance of a miniature garden.

The edges of the larger species of soft corals assume all sorts of fantastic shapes; some are produced into finger-like processes, others are folded and corrugated; some are irregularly lobed and leaf-like; while others again may bear a close resemblance to elephants' feet.

Many of the smaller ones, however, such as those belonging to the genus *Xenia*, are not only more erect and shapely, but they display the most delicate and pleasing colours, varying from a pale bluish-grey to a pale blue or lilac. These forms possess polyps with large expansive tentacles that are incapable of contraction; they form a permanent cluster at the summit of a broad, cylindrical stalk. Some are very beautiful.

All Alcyonarians, however, are not soft and flabby. There are two species which secrete strong supporting skeletons of lime and which the layman is likely to confuse with the true hard corals. One of these is the common organ-pipe coral, the other is known as the blue coral. Both display the eight pinnate tentacles characteristic of all Alcyonaria.

The organ-pipe coral has a skeleton consisting of parallel tubes with spaces between them about the width of the tubes or a little less, and they are connected at irregular intervals by horizontal platforms. Their name has been derived from the arrangement of these pipes which bear a striking resemblance to those of an organ. The whole skeleton is a bright red. Externally the coral is usually rounded or dome-shaped, and when the polyps are extended, as they frequently are to some extent even in the daytime, the surface is covered by a mantle of green, or more rarely greenish-brown. An organ-pipe coral with tentacles partially expanded is seen to the left of the starfish in Plate 37, and the reddish skeleton of another is seen in Plate 40 near the lower right-hand corner.

The other hard Alcyonarian, or blue coral, is less abundant, and, unlike the organ-pipe coral which occurs widely distributed over reef flats as well as in deeper water, is usually found in situations where it is permanently submerged, although occasionally it may be exposed for brief intervals at very low spring tides. It is more common towards the northern area of the Barrier Reef, particularly in the region of Torres Strait, and occurs in the form of erect clumps of irregular vertical plates from a foot to about two feet high. Externally this Alcyonarian is a dull bluish-grey but when broken the interior is found to be a bright indigo blue which, like the red of the organ-pipe coral, is retained with but little fading for long after the coral is dead.

There is another class of corals known as horny corals which comprise two main types, the Gorgonids and the Antipatharians. They bear a close resemblance to shrubs that have shed their leaves; the horny consistency of the branches in many species gives them the appearance of twigs with a smooth bark, and their flexibility renders the similarity all the more striking.

The two types can usually be at once distinguished by the disposition of their branches; in the Gorgonids they are arranged in one plane like the ribs of a fan but without their regularity, while in the Antipatharians they grow out in all directions. One of the commonest of the Gorgonids is a bright red colour; it is illustrated in the frontispiece where it is seen extending upwards from the centre of the picture. If one of the Gorgonids is examined closely its surface will be seen to be thickly perforated with minute depressions which are the homes of the individual polyps; when expanded these are found to have eight feather-like tentacles resembling those of Alcyonarian corals but they are much smaller and for the most part are colourless and almost transparent.

The Antipatharians are usually black; although flexible they have an exceedingly dense structure, and the polyps have only six tentacles. Pieces of black horny corals are shown in Plate 18, fig. 1*b*; they have leaf-shaped oysters attached to them by finger-like processes.

These horny corals are found almost exclusively in the deeper water beyond the reef edge where they are sometimes gathered by divers when searching for pearl or trochus shell, or they may be collected by means of a dredge. On account of their delicate structure they are frequently dislodged by storms and washed up on the beaches. A very curious form which is occasionally washed ashore in the southern area of the reef consists of branches that are composed of alternate layers of a fluted limy deposit and a narrower one of a dense black horny material; it resembles white and black beads threaded on a stem and then fused together.

The red coral of commerce is an Alcyonarian coral and occurs in the Mediterranean where it is gathered by divers. Like the black horny corals described above it has an extremely dense structure and polishes like the finest marble.

AGENTS OF DESTRUCTION

One might be pardoned for imagining that corals, growing as they do in such profusion over a widespread area, are very hardy animals. In many respects, on the contrary, they are extremely delicate. Given an environment to their liking where they are never exposed to the air nor pounded by the action of waves; where the temperature is uniformly warm; where the density of the water, uninfluenced by fresh water poured into the sea by coastal streams, remains consistently high; where there is little sediment; where the light streaming through the water is bright; where there is an abundance of food and oxygen; then corals will grow in great profusion and spread rapidly. But if this balance is markedly disturbed in any one direction they are doomed. A coral, if handled on the reef, at once gives off a slimy mucus; if removed and placed in a tub of sea-water the water quickly becomes obscured by a copious secretion of this milky liquid and in a very short time the coral will die.

Coral cannot withstand long exposure to the air, and when it grows to such a height that ordinary tides uncover it the uppermost branches or layers do not long survive.

The resistance of the many varieties to sediment varies greatly; it is governed largely by the capacity of the coral to remove it. If the coral were powerless to remove sediment from its surface, which even in the clearest water of the reef is never absent, it would quickly choke to death.

Corals cannot move from place to place to avoid it and so they are forced to sweep it away mechanically. Covering the whole of the surface of corals are minute hairs, or cilia, which are in constant vibration; their movements are so controlled that they are continually conveying sediment towards the edge where it falls from the surface. This may be very strikingly demonstrated in the mushroom coral. Even if it is so covered with sediment as to obscure the surface of the coral the vigorous and sustained beating of the hairs gradually passes the sediment to the outer edge and in a relatively short time the whole of the surface is freed from it. Now, the mushroom coral, lying usually on the surface of the sand in shallow water, is liable by the shifting of the sand to become partially or wholly embedded, but this rarely occurs for, if it finds itself sinking into the sand, it can force its way upwards by the vigorous beating of its strong cilia till it is once more free on the surface.

In some corals in which the tentacles are not strongly developed and which therefore have a very limited capacity for gathering food by their agency, the main function of the cilia is to collect the particles of food and pass them to the mouth. In others, again, the cilia have a dual function to perform; they beat more rapidly in the direction of the mouth when the polyp is feeding, and they beat in the opposite direction when it becomes necessary to remove sediment.

Cyclones and hurricanes play tremendous havoc with corals growing in situations exposed to their influence. The terrific pounding action of the waves tears the branching corals to pieces over wide areas, and the more solid forms are dislodged and thrown about from place to place. Havoc and destruction follow in the wake of every cyclone, and

PLATE 8.

A BORDER OF "LAVENDER" CORAL

LOWER SURFACE OF A CORAL BOULDER
ENCRUSTED WITH MARINE GROWTHS

instances are known where practically the whole of the coral on a reef has been destroyed overnight.

The effect of storms and cyclones can be seen on every reef that is bared by the tide. On the weather side great coral boulders are strewn about the reef; the majority will be found resting on the platform or rampart forming the reef crest, but occasionally they may be found from two to three hundred yards from the edge. These boulders were once great thriving Porites or perhaps brain corals growing on the outer slope of the reef, and the sheer force of the seas has lifted them bodily and rolled them on to the surface, where, exposed for long periods to the air, they quickly died. As these coral boulders weather they usually lose their rounded outline and develop hollows and depressions bordered by jutting edges that in many cases become encrusted with a black lichen, and so have received the name of "nigger-heads" (Plate 44, fig. 2), though their resemblance to the woolly heads of negroes is usually far from striking.

But it is not only the violent pounding action of the waves that causes the damage. In the tropical belt the rains are extraordinarily prolific; the falls are so concentrated over a small space of time that the surface waters remain almost fresh for some time afterwards, and corals cannot survive fresh water. In some situations great quantities of sand and mud are stirred up to be deposited over the coral everywhere; the sediment is too great to be handled by the coral, the strength of the cilia is overtaxed, and vast quantities are smothered.

Particularly is the influence of fresh water felt in the neighbourhood of the mouths of rivers on the eastern coast of Queensland. These rivers flood, and enormous quantities of fresh water and silt flow out to sea, depositing the silt over the bottom for miles around. Coral has little chance of flourishing in such situations.

Thus cyclones leave chaos in their train. To-day we see a long succession of gardens; the coral is growing, flourishing, decorating the whole area with its beauty; to-morrow desolation stalks everywhere, the coral is torn up and distributed in untidy masses over the reef, there quickly to waste and die—to form a coral graveyard.

The life of coral, like that of every other animal on the reef, is one long struggle for existence: it is ever growing, growing upwards; building, building solidly; ever consolidating its gains, ever extending the area of the reef. It is winning. But it is not winning unaided. Without assistance it would remain so many distinct units to be battered about by the restless sea whose fury it can withstand only by its fusion into solid buttresses. The chemical action of sea-water itself probably tends to cement adjacent masses, but far more is probably accomplished by encrusting growths which, enveloping loose corals, bind them into a united whole. Of tremendous importance in this direction are the coralline Algae (seaweeds) known as Nullipores. These Algae secrete a lime as solid as that of the coral itself; indeed, as they creep as an enveloping sheet over the coral on the reef edge, where they are most active, they bear a superficial resemblance to encrusting coral. Although they grow usually as a thin layer, others may creep over their surface till they are several layers thick and they are thereby enabled to resist the force of the heaviest of seas.

A group of minute single-celled animals known as Foraminifera, which occur in myriads everywhere about a coral reef (and practically everywhere in the sea for that matter), are also playing an important part in consolidating the reef. Their skeletons accumulate in crevices and between adjacent coral boulders and their ultimate fusing tends to cement individual corals and coral boulders into a more solid mass.

And so the coral consolidates its gains. But the struggle is a hard one for besides the forces of nature, the wind and the rain with their accompanying agents of destruction, there are many animals that are continually undermining it; mussels and other bivalves bore into it; sea-urchins rasp pockets in its surface for their protection; and worms excavate tubular channels which they make their homes.

CORAL ROCK

How are we to account for the solid rock lining portion of the foreshores of coral islands that everywhere else are composed of loose coral sand? Most coral islands of any great age have some portion of their foreshores composed of solid rock. At Heron Island, for instance, such a rocky formation extends along the southern shore for some hundreds of yards between the upper and lower limits of the tide. This rock has every appearance of once forming a solid mass several feet thick; it is now divided by longitudinal and transverse fissures into great blocks, though they are still for the most part united along their bases. Its slope conforms to that of the sandy beach that everywhere else fringes the island; it is composed of what was once loose sand that has become consolidated by the cementing action of lime. Heavy rain soaks through the coral sand of the island dissolving the lime in its train; at low tide it seeps through the sand that has been exposed to the air; the heat of the sun evaporates it, leaving a deposit of limestone to fill up the spaces between the grains of sand and to bind them together as a thin layer on the surface. And so during each wet period more and more lime has been available to carry on this cementing action till the united sand grains formed a solid rock several feet in thickness. Meanwhile the action of the waves and the rain have combined to weather it into fissures. On some coral islands the fissures have completely penetrated it, resulting in a great quantity of loose flat boulders which the seas have thrown about into irregular masses. A splendid example of this is to be seen on the shore of Wilson Island, in the Capricorns.

GROWTH-RATE OF CORALS

Although the experiments that have been made to determine the growth-rate of corals are of a limited character, all have given unmistakable evidence that they grow very rapidly. Some large corals measured by Saville-Kent at Thursday Island were again measured twenty-three years later when it was found that the diameter of a brain coral had increased from thirty inches to seventy-four inches, and a Porites (one of the densest of corals) from nineteen feet to twenty-two feet nine and a half inches.

In the Indian Ocean it has been estimated that it would take about a thousand years to form a reef eighty-seven feet deep, and in the vicinity of Samoa, in the Pacific, it has been calculated that a reef would extend to a depth of about eighty-one feet in the same time. In neither calculation, however, was allowance made for the decay of the corals and their destruction by gales and other agencies.

Surprisingly rapid growth was recorded by the British Barrier Reef Expedition at Low Island as the result of a series of experiments that allowed of accurate measurements being made. In some cases the corals almost doubled their size in the course of six months.

PLATE 9.

A FLYING FISH IN FLIGHT

LONG-SPINED SEA-URCHINS IN A CORAL POOL

Photos: T. C. Roughley.

PLATE 10.

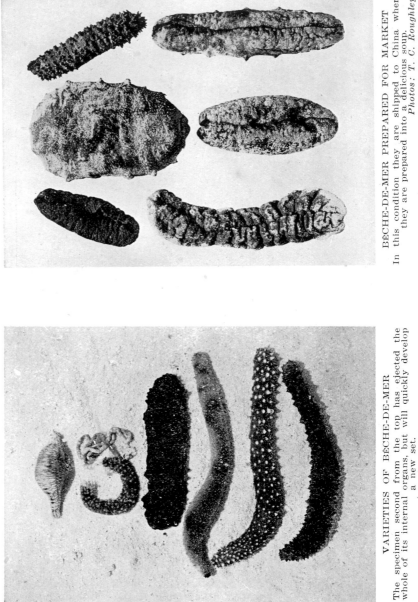

BÊCHE-DE-MER PREPARED FOR MARKET

In this condition they are shipped to China where they are prepared into a delicious soup.

Photos: T. C. Roughley.

VARIETIES OF BÊCHE-DE-MER

The specimen second from the top has ejected the whole of its internal organs, but will quickly develop a new set.

FOR elegance and grace, for delicacy of form and quiet
beauty of colour, the sea anemones of the Barrier Reef
have a charm unrivalled by any other form of life to be
found there. They are the flowers of the reef, and many
bear a close resemblance to the beautiful blooms of chrysanthemums and cactus dahlias (Plates 15, 16, 17, 22, 23).
Indeed, so close is their resemblance to flowers with their
tentacles waving like dainty petals, that many visitors to the
reef do not associate them with animal life at all.

Yet they are animals, and their resemblance to flowers is
a superficial one only. In structure they are essentially
similar to the coral polyps already described; indeed, when
some of the larger solitary types of corals are fully expanded
it is sometimes difficult to determine without a close examination whether they are corals or anemones, and an even
closer resemblance is displayed by some of the Alcyonarian
or soft corals. But, unlike the majority of corals, anemones
have not the faculty of secreting a limy skeleton and therefore they remain always soft and fleshy.

The body of a sea anemone is usually cylindrical in shape;
the lower surface is attached to rock so securely that its
removal is difficult, but it is able to creep slowly over the
surface if it desires to change its position. In the smaller
kinds the free end is rounded and fringed with tentacles,
but in the larger examples it may be expanded into a great

E

disk folded and pleated at the edges and covered everywhere, except in the central region where the mouth is situated, with a great number of tentacles that are in continual
movement as they curl and unfold in search of particles of
food borne along by the current. Food is collected in an
exactly similar manner to that employed by the coral polyps;
each tentacle is provided with a great number of stinging
or nettle cells that paralyse living prey and then pass it
from one to the other towards the mouth which opens
wide to receive it.

The stomach, as in the corals, is a closed sac divided by
radial partitions which serve for the absorption of the food
and for the development of the reproductive elements.
Digestion is rapid, and the remnants of the food are passed
out through the mouth to be carried by the tentacles to the
edge where they are dropped off.

The anemones of the Barrier Reef are remarkable for
their large size, their beauty of colour, and for the diversity
of their tentacles. Sea anemones are widely distributed
throughout the world, but in more temperate regions, as
for instance in Port Jackson, they rarely exceed a diameter
of two or three inches; on the Barrier Reef, however, they
are commonly seen up to twelve inches, and some when fully
expanded may measure up to eighteen inches or even two
feet.

Their colours are extremely variable, even in the one
species, and although the giants of the tribe are usually
somewhat drab, varying from grey to green or brown, many
of the smaller kinds are very brilliant.

The stinging cells, which serve to paralyse their prey,
are in the great majority of sea anemones incapable of penetrating human skin and they may therefore be handled with
impunity, but there are one or two kinds that sting as

severely as a nettle and may leave a rash on the skin that persists for several days. These stinging anemones differ from their innocuous relatives (innocuous, of course, only so far as human beings are concerned) in the arrangement of their tentacles; instead of covering an expanded disk they radiate outwards from the region of the mouth and branch extensively like tufts of seaweed, which they resemble very closely. So effective is the disguise that many creatures are trapped before they realize their mistake and, paralysed by a battery of darts, pay the supreme penalty for their defective observation.

One of the most curious features of the anemones of the reef is the intimate association with them of small, brilliantly coloured fish and crustaceans. Some of the larger kinds have almost invariably one or two fish, from two to three inches long, snuggling amongst their tentacles, hiding amongst their folds, or even occasionally entering their stomachs. There is no doubt that the fish, which in some extraordinary way are perfectly immune from the anemone's stings, benefit greatly from this association, for they are afforded wonderful protection from their enemies, and they pick off such food as they require from the anemone's tentacles as it passes towards its mouth. But if a feeling of insecurity develops as it moves about the surface, it may hide amongst the folds of the anemone with its head only showing at the surface, like small boys I have seen hiding in the folds of their mothers' skirts when skirts were worn full and billowy, or it may find complete protection in the anemone's stomach. If a stick is thrust into the mouth of a giant anemone it is not uncommon for one and sometimes two of these fish to swim out, but they almost invariably make back again as soon as the stick is removed.

These anemone fish are always brightly coloured and

conspicuously marked; some possess a ground colour of brilliant scarlet, their deep bodies crossed by two or sometimes three bands of pure white which may be edged with black, while one common species is a deep brown with the lower surface of the head and the dorsal, pectoral, and caudal (tail) fins brilliant orange, and with a broad pale blue band crossing the head vertically behind the eye. Incidentally, it may be remarked that this band gives the fish a rather grotesque appearance; it bears a striking resemblance to a bandage round the head of a fish suffering from ear-ache, a likeness accentuated by the gloomy expression caused by the downward curvature of its mouth.

Now, these fish are frequently associated with anemones whose colour is very drab, and against such a background they are rendered very conspicuous. During the course of our wanderings over the reef we shall meet many animals that so blend with their surroundings as to make their detection extremely difficult; we shall find many others that adopt all sorts of curious devices to conceal themselves from their foes. Concealment is one of the greatest objectives of the marine life of the reef; how then can we account for the conspicuousness of the anemone fish? In its case camouflage is unnecessary for it is adequately protected by its intimate association with the anemone which is dreaded by all the other inhabitants of the reef, and it seems very probable that it serves as a lure to attract other forms of marine life within range of the anemone's batteries.

Although the benefits derived by the fish are quite obvious there has always been some doubt as to whether the anemone has received any advantage from the association, but some observations made recently on anemone fish kept in aquaria in Egypt seem to indicate that it is of very great service to its host. It was found that, although the fish spent most

PLATE 11.

ENCRUSTING CORAL OF DELICATE MAUVE IN A SETTING OF SEAWEEDS AND BRANCHING CORAL

of its time moving amongst the folds of the anemone, if another fish were introduced into the aquarium the anemone fish immediately attacked it and endeavoured to drag it towards the anemone's tentacles where, if the fish was small, it was immediately paralysed, but if comparatively large several contacts were necessary before paralysis was complete; in each case the fish was conducted to the anemone's mouth to be engulfed.

It would appear, therefore, that the anemone fish is an active hunter for its host; that it repays the anemone for the protection afforded by dragging prey to where the anemone can deal with it. But its duties do not cease there. After some hours the bones of the fish are ejected through the anemone's mouth and these the fish picks up and carries away. Possibly this is the reason why the fish is in the habit of exploring the kitchen to obtain some reward for its guile and labour.

In addition to these fish many anemones have constantly associated with them a small shrimp, which may be almost transparent and therefore exceedingly difficult to detect, or it may be brilliantly coloured to conform to that of the anemone for it appears to be able to regulate its colour at will. Then, too, a small crab is frequently found moving over the anemone's surface; like the shrimp it is almost transparent and is completely immune from the anemone's stings.

The food of anemones consists of a wide variety of marine life embracing amongst other forms small shrimp-like creatures, crabs, and fishes.

Some anemones, not satisfied with the defensive powers of their armature, accumulate on their tentacles sand and pieces of broken shells which aid in their concealment, while others may burrow beneath the sand or mud in the

intertidal zone, appearing at the surface during every
period of high tide.

One or two species, such as the blood-red waratah
anemone, habitually frequent damp situations on or beneath
stones where they are uncovered by the tide. During their
period of exposure their tentacles are completely retracted
and their bodies glisten a deep reddish-brown, but when
the water covers them they display their beautiful crimson
tentacles, which are continually on the move in search of
prey. These anemones are commonly seen in rocky situations where they may occur in clusters on many of the islands
of the reef, and they are also abundant on the coast of
New South Wales where the children usually refer to them
as "blood-suckers," under the impression that they will suck
the blood of the person handling them, an idea that doubtless originated from their blood-red colour. They attain
a diameter of about two inches and are, of course, perfectly
harmless.

Anemones have a very long life and may be kept in
aquaria for many years with very little attention. The
record for longevity is held by some individuals that have
been in captivity in Edinburgh for seventy-four years.

Sea anemones are a delightful feature of the aquaria in
the Taronga Park (Sydney) zoo where many beautiful examples with their attendant fishes may be seen. Some of these
have been obtained from the waters of Port Jackson and
others from Lord Howe and the Solomon Islands. When
they are first received they are usually a pale brown or green
but in the aquaria their colour gradually fades till at the end
of two or three months they are a pure fleecy white. They
may remain attached to one spot for weeks and at other times
may creep over the surface and change their position almost
daily. Those from Lord Howe Island and the Solomons

are fed every day on minced prawns, the fine particles being sprinkled over the surface of the tentacles. The local anemones, however, are not partial to prawns but they relish a diet of oysters, and three times a week a whole oyster is dropped on to the tentacles of each individual where it is at once enveloped by them and conveyed to the mouth.

On account of their stinging capabilities anemones are avoided by other animals of the reef, but there is at least one exception; the beautiful naked-gilled molluscs known as Nudibranchs or sea-slugs (Plate 39) attack them by rasping pieces out of their bodies. These animals, too, appear to be immune from the stings; indeed, they make use of them by storing them in projecting lobes on their upper surface where they are kept in reserve to stun their own foes in case of attack.

The association of sea anemones with hermit and other crabs is one of the most curious features of the life of the reef, but we shall discuss that when dealing with the crab life (Chapter IX).

CHAPTER SEVEN

Sea-stars, Sea-urchins and Bêche-de-mer

STARFISH of diverse sizes, forms, and colours abound everywhere on the reef flats from the most northern to the most southern limits of the Barrier; in size they may vary from an inch or less to over a foot in diameter, from a fraction of an ounce to several pounds in weight; in form they range from kinds with small bodies and long, radiating arms to those with squat, bulky, cushion-shaped bodies and arms reduced to mere vestiges.

Undoubtedly the most common, most conspicuous and most widely distributed is a large blue starfish that abounds on almost every reef (Plate 24); it is conspicuous by its size, which varies from about eight to twelve inches across the arms (smaller ones are rarely if ever seen on the reef flats), and by its colour which is a cobalt blue of wonderful purity with inconspicuous lighter spots distributed everywhere over the surface. The body of this starfish is reduced to a minimum; it is formed by the junction of the five long arms which are almost three-quarters of an inch thick at their bases. Most starfish have a tendency to conceal themselves amongst the coral or under boulders in the daytime but this blue *Linckia* is usually found lying on the sand in most exposed situations.

Equally striking though far less abundant is a bright red species with a much larger body and with arms less well defined. Extending along the surface of each arm is a series of rounded black protuberances which add considerably to its beauty and help to throw it into even greater relief.

Far more substantial than either of the above is a species that has the arms reduced to bluntly triangular projections, while the body is extremely bulky and resembles a pentagonal cushion. It is known generally as the pincushion starfish and may attain a diameter of upwards of a foot and a weight of several pounds. Its colour is very variable, ranging from olive-green to reddish-brown, variously spotted and mottled on the upper surface.

Thus amongst the giants of the Barrier Reef starfish we have an extreme divergency of shape, and the multitude of smaller species will be found to conform more or less closely to one or another of them.

Looked at from above, starfish are seen to be covered with a hard, leathery integument, but if turned over they will be found to have a groove extending along the whole length of each arm and meeting at the centrally situated mouth. These grooves are bordered by a great number of small, muscular tubes that can be stretched out or withdrawn at will; they are known as tube-feet and by their means the starfish is able to crawl about, though always very sluggishly. The tube-feet are remarkable little structures, unique in the animal world on account of the fact that their activities are dependent on a supply of water for their expansion and contraction. When the animal requires them to expand it pumps them full of water which distends them greatly, and when it is necessary to contract them the water is withdrawn. Each is provided with a sucker-like extremity and walking is accomplished by pushing a series in the direction it is desired to take, attaching them to the surface and then contracting them to draw the body forward. The suction of the tube-feet is remarkably strong and if a starfish is pulled from a rock many of the feet will probably be found to remain adherent to it.

Equally characteristic are the feeding habits of a starfish. Much of the food is conducted to the mouth by a sort of hand-to-hand movement of the tube-feet, but there are occasions when prey is encountered much too large to pass through the mouth. Under similar circumstances most other animals would bite or rasp the surface to remove pieces sufficiently small to handle, but the starfish has not the means at its disposal for doing either of these things and so it performs a far more remarkable feat—it forces its baggy stomach through its mouth, envelops the prey with it and digests it before again withdrawing its stomach into its interior.

In Europe and America certain species of starfish are a menace to oysters and do considerable damage to those lying loose on the beds. For a long time the manner in which the starfish opened the oyster remained a mystery, but it is now known to envelop itself round the shell and, attaching its tube-feet to both valves, it exerts a firm and steady pressure in opposite directions. The large adductor muscle which holds the two valves of the shell together, although very powerful, gradually tires under the continual strain and at last relaxes, allowing the valves of the shell to gape. The starfish then inserts its protrusible stomach into the oyster and dissolves away the flesh.

Naturally the oyster-growers wage war on the starfish. At one time, whenever one was brought up in the dredge it was promptly chopped in two and thrown overboard. Little did they realize that they were thereby increasing the pests they were so anxious to destroy, for each half is capable of developing into a complete starfish. Having learnt this, the oyster-growers now either take the starfish ashore or drown it in fresh water. Fortunately there is no evidence of the killing of oysters by starfish in Australian waters.

The regenerative powers of starfish are very marked. If the arms are cut off with a portion of the central disk attached each will eventually develop into a fully-formed starfish; if an arm is broken off it at once begins to grow again, and it is very common to find on the Barrier Reef starfish that have been mutilated by fishes and others of their foes in various stages of redevelopment of the lost parts. One may even sometimes see an arm with a small central disk at one end and four buds beginning to grow out from its edge.

Some starfish of the Barrier habitually frequent the inter-tidal zone, and as the tide recedes they burrow just beneath the sand where their star-shaped contour may be betrayed by a slight bulge at the surface; thus they escape the atten-tion of wading birds which are ever fossicking over the reef at low water.

Although the great majority of starfish possess five arms, some species commonly found on the reef are provided with six, seven, or even more.

BRITTLE-STARS

Closely related to the starfish and far more active are the brittle-stars, which may be found under almost every boul-der of the reef. From a button-like disk long, flexible, serpentine arms radiate outwards for a distance of from fifteen to twenty times the diameter of the disk; they are extremely brittle (hence the name) and the animal is cap-able of snapping them, or portions of them, off at will. Indeed, so fragile are they that it is difficult to collect a speci-men entire no matter how carefully it is handled. Each portion continues to wriggle when detached and may crawl away some distance; the animal loses no time, however, in replacing the lost parts.

One of the commonest brittle-stars is olive-green or brown with a double line of white spots edged with black radiating from the centre of the disk to the bases of the five arms. An occasional specimen, however, will be found with very striking colour patterns. Each arm may attain a length of about twelve inches.

SEA-URCHINS

Another relative of the starfish is the sea-urchin, of which many interesting kinds are very prolific throughout the area of the reef. In the sea-urchins the same radial arrangement obtains but they are not provided with arms, their soft parts being covered by a hard, limy, rounded case which is beset with numerous projecting spines of variable length. The case or corona of the sea-urchin is frequently found washed up on beaches and is often referred to as a "sea-egg"; it is made up of a great number of small plates, and in life these are covered by a thin film of living tissue which continually adds to their substance to allow for the increased accommodation demanded by the animal inside.

Food is gathered by means of tube-feet that project through small holes in the case; these are provided with a water-system that allows of their expansion and contraction as in the starfish. The food is conveyed to the mouth, situated in an opening of the shell in the centre of the lower surface, where it is ground up in an elaborate mill known as "Aristotle's lantern," the five teeth of which can be seen projecting at the surface.

Situated between the rigid spines on the upper surface are large numbers of smaller flexible spines provided with claws. These are of several kinds and have different functions to perform; the duty of one type is to seize any foreign matter that lodges between the spines and to pass it from one to the other till it is completely removed from the sur-

PLATE 12.

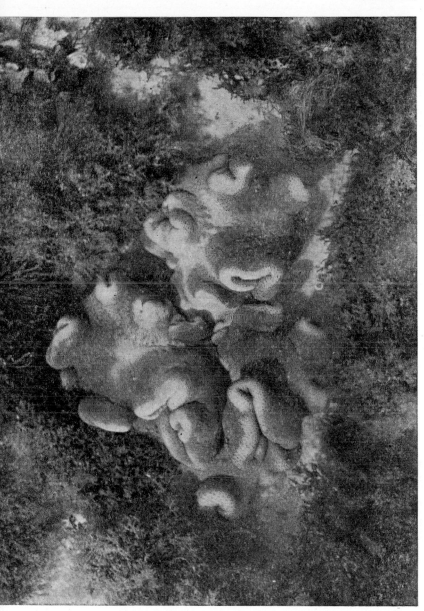

A SOFT OR ALCYONARIAN CORAL IN A GARDEN OF SEAWEEDS

face; they are therefore cleansing agents and their function is a very necessary one for without them the animal would accumulate much sediment. Another type performs a defensive function. The principal enemy of the sea-urchin is its relative the starfish, and when the latter begins to encircle the sea-urchin with its arms, the rigid spines of the urchin are moved aside in order that the defensive spines may come in contact with the tube-feet of the starfish; they at once grip them and leave the claws in the wound. Usually this causes the starfish to withdraw, but it may continually return to the attack until eventually the sea-urchin has lost all its weapons.

The sea-urchin is enabled to crawl about slowly by the movements of its spines which work on ball-and-socket joints under muscular control; they are aided by the tube-feet, and occasionally by the tips of the jaws.

The most conspicuous sea-urchin of the Barrier Reef is that known as the long- or needle-spined sea-urchin. It is usually found in clusters and upwards of a hundred may be seen congregated together in one pool. It is black or purplish-black in colour and its spines grow to a length of ten or twelve inches; they are as sharp as needles, barbed, and extremely fragile; on the slightest touch they break off in the flesh and their removal is difficult. Although reputed to be poisonous I have never been able to detect any definite poisonous properties associated with them. I have several times had their points penetrate my fingers and, although their barbed structure renders their extraction a matter of some difficulty, nevertheless they can usually be removed with a needle, and if the wound is carefully cleansed with methylated spirit my experience would seem to indicate that no ill effects are likely to ensue.

A cluster of needle-spined sea-urchins may be rather

attractive objects in a pool (Plate 9, fig. 2); arranged in a circle on the upper surface of each is a series of five eyes, "precious jewels of sparkling blue."

Numbers of small fishes may occasionally be seen sheltering amongst the spines, and the protection afforded them would appear to be wellnigh complete, for with such a defensive armature this sea-urchin is probably invulnerable.

Of a very different type is that known as the slate-pencil urchin (Plate 25, fig. 2) the spines of which are very stout and bluntly pointed. Although less formidable than those of the needle-spined urchin, their disposition and hardness form a very effective added protection to an animal whose soft parts are already enclosed by limy plates.

There are many other kinds of sea-urchins common on the reef, some with long spines, others with comparatively short ones, but we shall have to content ourselves with a mention of one or two only of the more interesting types.

Some burrow in sand, and in order to facilitate their progress the spines are all pointing the one way like those of a hedgehog. As they burrow the sand is continually entering the mouth and the particles of food accompanying it are sifted out.

Others gather round themselves pieces of seaweed, dead leaves of mangroves, or other debris, and rely on these for protection as they wander over the reef.

And then there is a type which burrows for shelter into hard coral rock by a constant movement of its spines which may be partially worn away in the process.

In Mediterranean countries certain kinds of sea-urchins are regularly marketed as food, the reproductive organs being considered of delicious flavour—*frutta di mare* (fruit of the sea) as they are described in Naples.

In Australia they are never eaten, but there is no reason

why several of the larger kinds should not be very palatable. We eat oysters raw; why not sea-urchins? If one may judge from Banfield's opinion of the edible qualities of the long-spined sea-urchin, there is at least one species on the reef that has its virtues. Thus he describes it:

"The flavour! Ah, the flavour! It surpasseth the delectable oyster. It hath more of the savour and piquancy of the ocean. It clingeth to the palate and purgeth it of grosser tastes. It recalleth the clean and marvellous creature whose life has been spent in cool coral grottoes, among limestone and the salty essences of the pure and sparkling sea, and if you be wise and devout and grateful, you forthwith give praise for the enjoyment of a new and rare sensation."

BÊCHE-DE-MER

Another close relative of the starfish, but at first sight bearing little resemblance to it, is the bêche-de-mer, which has many aliases such as trepang, sea-cucumber, or the even more descriptive title of sea-sausage. Some of these terms are self-explanatory for this elongated animal bears some resemblance in shape to a cucumber or giant sausage (Plate 10, fig. 1), but a word of explanation is necessary in the case of the others. The term "bêche-de-mer" is the French form of the Portuguese *bicho-do-mar*, which signifies a sea-worm, the name given to the creature by the early Portuguese navigators in Indo-China seas, while "trepang" is the Malayan name for the animal.

Throughout the whole area of the Great Barrier Reef bêche-de-mer are extraordinarily prolific; on the sand-flats, amongst the coral, in the deeper water beyond the reef edge, they can be seen every few yards and against the white sand their dark outline is very conspicuous. In length they vary from a few inches to about two feet, the larger kinds usually being found in the deeper water; in colour they range from a mottled creamy-white through various shades of yellow, orange, and brown to black; the majority are dark and drab, while a very common species on the reef flats is jet black above and a bright crimson below.

During the daytime they may remain stationary on the sand for long periods though sometimes they may be seen crawling over the surface very slowly, for they are always sluggish in their movements, their progression being accomplished, like that of the starfish, by means of tube-feet which are expanded and contracted by a similar water pressure. These tube-feet are rarely seen when the animal is lifted out of the water for they are instantly retracted within the body.

If you are careful not to disturb the animal you may see it feeding. At one end a number of sticky tentacles fringing the mouth are thrust out and one by one they are withdrawn and pushed down the throat where the sand and other matter that adheres to them are removed; incessantly this process is going on, the sand passing in a continuous stream along the alimentary canal where the food material accompanying it is sifted and its nutriment absorbed, the sand itself passing out through an aperture (the anus) at the hinder end of the body.

Now pick one up and examine it; although unattractive it is perfectly harmless. It may be soft and flabby in the hands or perhaps thick-skinned and leathery, according to the type you happen to have chosen. Although when first handled it is probably inflated like a bladder, water usually oozes from the rear end till it is limp and flexible. Its powers of expansion and contraction are very marked and soon after its removal from the water it will probably be found to have shrunk to half its original size.

If you now replace the animal in the water you may pos-

PLATE 13.

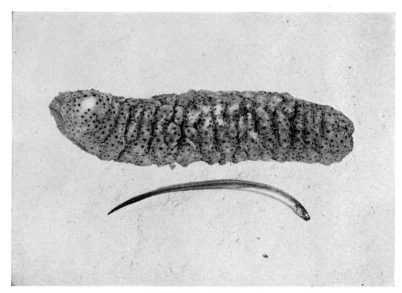

BÊCHE-DE-MER FISH
This fish habitually takes refuge in the hinder end of the gut of the bêche-de-mer above it.

A GREEN TURTLE DROWSING IN THE SUN
Photos: T. C. Roughley.

PLATE 14.

A GREEN TURTLE COMES ASHORE
Although the turtle is a powerful swimmer, when on land its movements
are very laboured.

Photo: T. C. Roughley.

A GREEN TURTLE LAYING ITS EGGS
The hind flippers have been drawn aside to expose the ovipositor.

Photo: Miss Hilda Geissmann.

sibly see a great stream of opalescent, bluish-white threads issuing from the hinder end of its body; they appear never-ending and spread out in the water in all directions, adhering to everything they touch (Plate 26, fig. 1). If the animal is left alone many of them may be withdrawn into its body, but if it is further molested they may continue to stream out till eventually the whole of them are discarded. Bêche-de-mer that exude these sticky threads are frequently referred to as "cotton-fish" or "cotton-spinners"; the threads of some of the larger kinds, however, are much thicker than the coarsest cotton; they are more of the thickness of darning wool, but smooth and glistening.

Although bêche-de-mer do not appear to be much sought after as food by any of the other inhabitants of the reef there seems to be little doubt that these threads serve to confuse and entangle such enemies as may attack them; apparently realizing this they rarely bother to make any effort to conceal themselves.

There are one or two species, however, which take the precaution of covering their bodies with a heavy sprinkling of sand thereby rendering themselves far less conspicuous.

Now, we have seen that a brittle-star if molested may snap its arms to fragments and later grow entirely new ones; this is probably a protective device to give the animal (or what remains of it) an opportunity of crawling away while its adversary is busy consuming the portions broken off. The bêche-de-mer cannot snap itself in pieces but it adopts an even more extraordinary course if strongly or continually irritated; it may eject through the hinder end of its body the whole or a large portion of its internal organs; these can be seen alongside the specimen second from the top in Plate 10, fig. 1. When I was preparing to photograph this group the individuals persisted in crawling out

F

of the field of view and with a glass rod I had just as continually to arrange them, till apparently irritated beyond endurance the animal referred to evacuated the whole of its inside.

That is remarkable enough; but in the course of a short time a creature that has thus mutilated itself will regenerate a completely new set of organs, and this is all the more to be wondered at when it is realized that until a new intestine is developed the animal is unable to obtain any nourishment. It has been recorded of one individual that within nine days of its complete evisceration it had regenerated the whole of its internal organs with the exception of those necessary for reproduction.

But that is not all. An occasional bêche-de-mer may be found harbouring one or several fish up to six inches in length in the hind portion of its gut. Now, the bêche-de-mer breathes through the opening situated at the posterior end of its body; sea-water is continually being drawn in to circulate through a branching organ known as the respiratory tree, and, as it opens to breathe, this thin, eel-like fish (Plate 13, fig. 1) slips in backwards and it may be seen shortly afterwards thrusting its head out, and, if disturbed, withdrawing it rapidly. The fish, glistening olive-green along the back and silvery along the belly, is smooth and scaleless, and slightly flattened from side to side. It is afforded wonderful protection in the unpopular bêche-de-mer (unpopular, that is, as a diet for other denizens of the reef, though as we shall see in Chapter XVII, it is in great demand by the Chinese for conversion into soup); and it receives an abundant and continually fresh supply of water, but it must leave its shelter when hunger drives it to seek its food.

A closely related fish habitually seeks shelter in the pearl oyster; swimming between the gaping valves of the shell it takes up its lodgings between the mantles where it is afforded abundant protection, but occasionally it makes a mistake and finds itself between one of the mantle folds and the shell; here it may be imprisoned till it dies and the oyster then proceeds to secrete mother-of-pearl over it till it is completely entombed in a pearly coffin. We shall see later that pearls are formed in just a similar manner by the oyster depositing layer after layer of this pearly substance over a grain of sand, a small piece of shell or a minute parasite which sets up an irritation. For many centuries the Chinese have taken advantage of a similar faculty in the freshwater mussel by inserting between the mantle and the shell a small porcelain image (a Buddha was a favourite subject) which becomes coated with mother-of-pearl, and at one time there was a considerable traffic in these shells with Western peoples.

A striking and curious relative of the bêche-de-mer is a long, snake-like inhabitant of weedy flats and coral crevices which, although found throughout the whole extent of the reef, is more common in the northern area. This creature, known as *Synapta*, may attain a length when fully extended of six feet, or it may contract itself to less than half that length. If you pick one of them up you will find that its skin tends to stick to the fingers; embedded in it are myriads of spicules shaped exactly like miniature anchors and these serve to give the animal a grip as it moves over the reef. If you grasp it in the middle of its body you will find the extremities of the animal hanging on each side distended with water, the portion you are holding consisting of little else than a flabby, sticky skin. Indeed, the animal seems to be but a skin full of water. Yet its organization is very similar to that of the bêche-de-mer; at one end is a ring of tentacles which continually pass sand into the mouth to be carried through the long intestine which opens at the hinder end of the body.

If handled roughly, the body may contract at one or more places and fall to pieces, but the portion with the head attached may eventually develop into a new individual. Although the sacrifice has been great the life of the animal may in this way have been saved.

The colour of *Synapta* is very variable; it may be pale reddish-brown with darker bands and blotches or it may be a combination of greyish and greenish tints.

Now, during the course of this chapter we have had occasion to refer to the capacity of such animals as starfish and bêche-de-mer to regenerate lost parts after a form of mutilation that would be fatal to many other animals, but, although this faculty of regeneration is of undoubted benefit to the individuals of the race, it cannot be stated with any degree of certainty just how it has arisen. On the one hand it is thought possible that it may be a survival of the normal asexual method of reproduction common to the more lowly forms of life, and on the other hand that it has been acquired as a means of escape from enemies. That the sacrifice of portion of the body allows of the escape of the remainder is quite evident, but it cannot be said with any assurance that it has developed by a process of natural selection as a result of the benefit this has conferred on the race. We shall meet further interesting examples of the regeneration of lost parts when we are dealing with crabs, whose limbs have a definite breaking-plane where they can be snapped off at will and without any risk to the life of the animal.

PLATE 15.

AN ANEMONE GARDEN

Many sea anemones of the Great Barrier Reef resemble chrysanthemums or cactus dahlias.

*The Turtles
Come Ashore*

ABOUT the year 1898 a certain adventurer, Louis de Rougemont by name, visited the north-western coast of Australia and lived for a time with the blacks. On his return to England he unfolded some remarkable tales of what he had seen, and amongst other things he told of how he had ridden turtles in the sea. This was altogether too much; his readers might perhaps be prepared to accept an account of a huge sea-serpent with rearing mane careering through the sea, but a tale of a turtle with a man on its back—impossible, ridiculous. The world had produced one Baron Munchausen and that was enough. Poor old de Rougemont died discredited, denounced.

Yet if his denouncers had paid a visit to one of the islands of the Great Barrier Reef in midsummer they could have enjoyed many a ride, as hundreds now do every year. Indeed, turtle-riding is regarded as one of the attractions of the reef during the summer months, when the females come ashore to lay their eggs. As they make back towards the sea, huge turtles weighing several hundredweight may be seen carrying tourists of both sexes. Now, it is easy enough to ride a turtle over sand, but to retain your seat when it reaches the sea is another matter, for it is necessary to keep its head above water by sitting well aft, otherwise it will plunge below to your complete discomfiture and the delight of your fellows.

Turtles are a feature of the life of the Great Barrier Reef from Torres Strait in the north to the Capricorns in the south. Although there are possibly four or five species in these waters, three only are very abundant; these are the green or edible turtle, the hawksbill or tortoise-shell turtle, and the loggerhead.

The loggerhead is the largest of the three and may attain a weight of fifteen hundred pounds; it is characterized by a relatively large and powerful head and a pugnacious disposition to which it is likely to give full vent if molested; when harpooned it has been known to leave the marks of its beak in the gunwale of a boat. It is a carnivorous species and lives on fish and shellfish; its flesh is rank, strong, and repulsive to whites but is relished by the blacks.

The hawksbill turtle never attains a weight exceeding three hundred pounds; it has derived its name from its beak-like mouth, and like the loggerhead subsists on a diet of fish. The flesh is despised as food, but the turtle has been much hunted for its shell, or carapace, which produces the tortoise-shell of commerce. The shell consists of an arrangement of shields or plates, which overlap their neighbours for about a third of their surface, and in order to separate them the carapace is either immersed in boiling water or is heated over a fire. When first removed they are curved and keeled; they are flattened by the application of heat and pressure, though care must always be taken to see that the heat is not too great for it tends to darken the shell. When it is necessary to join the plates they are welded together in a vice when hot; the heat partially melts the surface and a union is formed that can scarcely be detected by the naked eye. Unlike the green turtle, about which we shall have much to say in a moment, the hawksbill appears to breed only in the northern area of the reef; its eggs are relatively small, about the size of marbles.

The green turtle (Plate 26, fig. 2) is by far the commonest turtle on the Great Barrier Reef; it can at once be distinguished from the hawksbill by the disposition of the shields of the carapace, which do not overlap but are joined at their edges. Although the shell in younger individuals is attractively mottled in browns, blues, and yellows, it is of little commercial value; but the turtle has been extensively hunted for its flesh, which is as tender as young veal and resembles it somewhat in flavour; it also yields a rich soup, the joy of the epicure. Several attempts have been made to commercialize the green turtle by the erection of soup-canning factories on one or two of the islands of the Capricorn Group, but in no instance was the venture a financial success. The turtles were captured when they came ashore during the summer months. Egg-laying occurs on scores of coral islands from Torres Strait to the Capricorns, but most of the recorded observations have been made in the latter group of islands.

Pairing takes place at the surface of the sea usually in October and November, and towards the end of October a few females will be found making ashore. The numbers continually increase till about the first half of January, after which they again begin to dwindle, and egg-laying ceases by about the end of February.

The female comes ashore usually at night. It is by no means as active on land as in the water, and the journey over the sand is a most laborious one. Pulling with the front flippers and heaving with the hind ones it lurches forward in a series of ungainly, ponderous shuffles, and after proceeding a few paces it usually rests awhile before continuing its journey. The tracks left in the sand are highly characteristic; the successive indentations of the flippers form a parallel row of scalloped furrows while the depressions made by the tail form a broken line between them. When, however, the turtle makes down the slope on its journey back to the water the effort at walking is not nearly so strenuous and the tail usually drags to form a continuous line. A study of the disposition of the marks of the flippers and the tail will at once indicate the direction the turtle was taking, whether from or towards the water, and this is always a valuable aid to the hunters who seek them for canning.

Having arrived at the summit of the beach well above the limit of the tide the turtle at once sets about building her nest. A spot free from shrubs or trees is chosen and the work of excavating begins. With a vigorous scooping of the front flippers the sand is thrown back and it is then shovelled behind the turtle by means of the hind flippers; the work is heavy and frequent spells are taken. When the depression is large enough to accommodate her whole body the task of digging the egg-pit is begun. From the base of the depression the sand is scooped out by means of the hind flippers to a depth of about eighteen and a diameter of about twelve inches; the hind flippers are then folded over the pit and the eggs are dropped into it (Plate 14, fig. 2).

The eggs are white and spherical, the shells are parchment-like in consistency, and they measure about one and one-third inches in diameter; they are not fragile like hens' eggs but may be dropped a considerable distance without breaking. They are laid at the rate of about four or five a minute at first but the rate is continually increased. The number laid at one sitting may vary from fifty to about two hundred, though the average clutch is about one hundred and twenty.

Turtle eggs are peculiar inasmuch as the white does not

coagulate when boiled; few white people can tolerate them, but they are regarded as a delicacy by the aborigines and by the Torres Strait islanders and neighbouring races.

When egg-laying has been completed the turtle at once proceeds to replace the sand, which is shovelled into the egg-pit and patted down by means of the hind flippers, and then the heaped sand is scooped back into the depression with both flippers; it is pressed and levelled at the surface, and, the task now completed, the turtle makes back to the water.

If, during the course of digging, the turtle meets with an obstruction such as a root of a tree she usually ceases her efforts and proceeds to another spot; in this way the one turtle may be responsible for several partially completed depressions.

The length of time the turtle is ashore to carry on these all-important duties varies from one to seven hours, the average being about two and a half hours. Each turtle may come ashore to lay her eggs several times during the course of one breeding-season, and in some cases may visit more than one island for the purpose, but there is some doubt whether each female lays every season. Upwards of fifty turtles have been seen ashore during one night, all females; indeed, they are never accompanied by the males though the latter are frequently seen close inshore, being readily distinguished by their relatively long tails, which may grow to a foot or more in length.

The eggs are hatched by the heat of the sun, and the incubation period is determined to a considerable extent by the temperature; it is shorter in the tropics, but in the Capricorns it varies from nine and a half to ten and a half weeks; there is considerable wastage during incubation for, on an average, only about fifty per cent of the eggs hatch out. The newly-hatched turtle measures about three inches in length,

and immediately it breaks through the shell it works its
way to the surface of the sand; if it happens to hatch during
daylight it will usually remain till nightfall before it crawls
out, for many gulls, herons, and terns await its passage to
the water, and they take heavy toll of young ones that undertake the journey during the day. But even at night its passage is a precarious one for sand crabs, alert and fleet of foot,
destroy large numbers. Nor are its perils over when it reaches
the water for there predacious fishes await its coming and
reap a rich harvest.

The incubation period may not be entirely uniform in each
batch of eggs, for the actual hatching may be spread over
two or three nights. Unlike their parents, which are vege-
tarians, the young turtles are carnivorous and subsist on a
diet of small fishes.

The growth-rate of green turtles has not been determined
with certainty, though they have been found to attain a
length of eight inches in the course of a year, and it is
thought that a turtle measuring three feet eight inches long
may possibly be about ten years of age.

The green turtle attains a length of upwards of four feet
and a weight of at least five hundred pounds. It is a powerful swimmer but, as we have seen, it shuffles along labori-
ously when on land; if turned on its back it is unable to right
itself and if left in this position it is certain to die. Its principal enemy is the shark which frequently does great damage
to the flippers and the tail, and probably also is responsible
for large pieces being torn from the carapace itself.

It is a harmless, trusting creature and may frequently be
seen during the winter basking in shallow pools of the reef
flats. Looking back over the years I cannot help feeling
amused at my first encounter with a turtle. I had been
spending much time stalking various animals on the reef,

such as fishes and things, and almost invariably they would dash for cover at the first sign of my approach, then one day I saw a short distance away what appeared to be a smooth, dome-shaped rock projecting just above the surface of the water in a shallow pool. Approaching more closely I saw it was the upper part of the shell of a large green turtle. Fortunately it was facing away from me, so I stole back and procured a camera. Fearing that I might frighten it I crept along cautiously on tiptoe to what I thought was a safe distance and secured a photograph. Having obtained one picture I made bold to creep along to get a side view; this it didn't seem to mind, so I photographed it from the front. Having depicted it from all angles I was not so much concerned whether it moved away, so I entered the water in order to obtain a more intimate picture of its head, and, approaching to within a couple of feet of it I was focusing the camera when it slowly opened its eyes and without displaying the slightest interest in me promptly went to sleep again!

Turtle soup and steaks were always regarded as a delicacy during my stay at Heron Island; without exception the tourists voted them delicious. To the aboriginal they were a feast from the gods; they particularly relished the fat-layered intestine after just bringing it to the boil in a bailer-shell, though usually the whole of the turtle was cooked in an inverted position in order that the carapace might retain all the juices. But I suggest we accept Banfield's invitation to an aboriginal "Kummaorie," of which he gives us the following details:

"A big fire is made and a dozen or so smooth stones about the size of saucers put on the embers to get red hot. In the meantime the turtle is killed, the head, neck, and sometimes the two fore flippers removed. The entrails and stomach are taken out, and after being roughly cleansed are put back into the cavity. A hole is scraped in the sand, and the turtle stuck tail-first into it, the sand being banked up so that it remains upright. Then the red-hot stones are lifted with sticks and dropped into the turtle, hissing and spluttering, and stirred about with a stout stick. Another hole has been scooped in the sand and paved with stones, upon which a roaring fire is made. When the stones are hot through, the fire is scraped away, and the steaming turtle eased down from its upright position, care being taken not to allow any of the gravy to waste, and carefully deposited on the hot stones— carapace down. Quickly, so that none of the 'smell' escapes, the whole is covered with leaves—native banana, native ginger, palms, etc., and over all is raised a mound of sand. In the morning the flesh is thoroughly cooked. The plastron (lower shell) is lifted off, and in the carapace is a rich, thick soup. No blood or any of the juices of the meat have gone to waste—the finest of meat extracts, the very quintessence of turtle, remains.

"What would your gourmands give for a plate of this genuine article? Who may say he has tasted turtle soup— pure and unadulterated—unless he has 'Kummaoried' his turtle to obtain it? With balls of grass the blacks sop up the brown oily soup, loudly smacking and sucking their lips to emphasize appreciation. Then there are the white flesh and the gluten, the best of all fattening foods. Having eaten to repletion for a couple of days, the diet palls, and they begin to speak in shockingly disrespectful terms of turtle."

PLATE 16.

SEA ANEMONES OF A COLOUR RARE AMONGST ANIMAL LIFE

GIANT crabs, pygmy crabs; land crabs, swimming crabs; armoured crabs, delicate crabs; hermit crabs, soldier crabs; crabs that feign death; crabs that cultivate gardens on their backs; crabs innumerable abound everywhere on the reef and the habits of many of them are almost unbelievably strange.

One might readily be pardoned for imagining that crabs, protected as they are with hard shells, would be amongst the boldest animals on the reef; one might reasonably expect that, armed in addition with powerful and effective nippers, they would move fearlessly about hurling defiance at all who dared to approach them. Yet, what do we find? They are amongst the most sensitive inhabitants of the reef, and elaborate and really extraordinary precautions are taken to conceal themselves from their enemies. Their efforts at concealment are wonderfully effective, yet they employ it not for defensive purposes alone, but as an aid to stalk their prey. And what an efficient aid it is! What chance has an animal during the course of its wanderings about the reef of knowing that a bunch of seaweed it is approaching is merely a garden growing round a crab that is biding its time to thrust out its powerful and ruthless nippers whose grip leaves no chance of escape?

SOLDIER CRABS

It is not necessary to seek them in the water, for whole armies of crabs may at times be found on the sand when the tide is out. Armies? Yes, the name soldier crab which has been bestowed on them has been derived from their habit of marching in formation. In battalions they march, now in line, now in mass formation, swaying and turning like an army at exercises. And then you approach them to find their manoeuvres are a sham; their morale is shattered in an instant and they retreat like a disordered rabble, each for himself and the devil take the hindmost. If those in front move too slowly, then those behind climb over them until the retreat becomes a confused mass of crabs. But, without shot or shell, their numbers dwindle rapidly until (if the pursuit is followed far enough) not a single crab of the thousands remains. They have dug themselves in. And what diggers! Reaching a spot where the sand is wet they disappear like magic; digging with the legs of one side they burrow like a corkscrew into the sand in a few seconds.

The body of the soldier crab is almost circular in outline, and its pale blue colour has been responsible for the name "bluebottle crab" being sometimes applied to it.

SAND CRABS

If you stroll along the sand surrounding a coral island you cannot fail to notice, irregularly disposed about the surface above, and to a less extent below, high-water level, numerous holes up to a couple of inches in diameter with a mound of sand radiating fan-shape from the entrance for a distance of perhaps two or three feet. Each of these is the home of a sand crab but the crab itself is rarely seen abroad during the daytime; it runs too great a risk of forming a tasty meal for the many keen-eyed birds that relish such morsels.

If, however, you light the sand ahead of you with a torch at night, when the birds are roosting, you will see the frightened crabs, white and ghost-like, scurrying for their burrows, or for the water, with the speed of the wind. No crab can run faster. If you are very quick you may catch one—and, perhaps, receive a painful wound for your trouble—but if the crab once reaches the sanctuary of its home you may as well seek your quarry elsewhere, for its burrow may extend three or four feet into the sand and then may turn to run horizontally. It burrows to a depth where the sand is moist, and if its home is covered by the tide the excavating must be done every time the tide recedes. Grabbing some sand between two of its legs it carries it to the surface in the form of a pellet, jerks it a foot or two away from the entrance, then back it proceeds for another load, always crawling sideways. When the burrow has been excavated to the required depth the crab begins the laborious task of compressing the internal wall to prevent the sand caving in; this it does by patting it with its larger nipper and pressing against it with its back.

The sand crab is extremely alert. With its eyes at the extremity of long, movable stalks it commands a panoramic view of its surroundings. Its food consists principally of minute crustaceans which are usually left on the surface of the sand after every tide; these it sifts after scooping the sand to its mouth with its claws; backing a pace it makes another scoop, and so feeds as it goes—or should we say, comes? In addition it is fond of carrion, and may act as an efficient scavenger when the carcasses of fishes or birds are washed up on the beach. The larger individuals prey upon the newly-hatched turtles as they make their way to the water, and, should their burrows happen to encounter a nest full of eggs they are prone to regard such a well-stored larder as a gift from the gods.

If the night is still and you remain very quiet, listening intently, you may hear a peculiar rasping sound emanating from the crabs or perhaps from the occupied burrows. This noise is made by rubbing a file-like surface on the upper portion of each claw against another near its base, but the purport of it is not known with certainty. On the one hand it is thought that it may serve as a "stand-off" signal, warning intruders that the burrow is occupied and trespassers will not be welcome within, or on the other hand it may be used as a mating call.

The sand crab can live for quite long periods out of water, for its gill chambers are richly supplied with blood-vessels and are adapted to enable them to extract oxygen from the air; they must be kept moist, however, and when roaming about the sand the crab will periodically make to the water for a "dip." It is often stated that this crab will drown if kept under water; my own experience has shown, however, that it will stand long immersion, and when placed in fresh water, which few crabs can long survive, it has outlived the great majority of those I have experimented with.

The sand crab is white or creamy white in colour and may attain a width of about nine inches across the outstretched legs.

FIDDLER CRABS

Each type of foreshore has its own form of crab—the sand crab on the sandy beaches and the fiddler or beckoning crab on the mud amongst the mangroves. Each is adapted to its own environment and "never the twain shall meet." Many of the islands between the Barrier and the coast in the northern half of the reef embrace mud-flats within their compass when the tide is low—soft, oozy mud, or, perhaps, a mixture of sand and mud, drab and uninviting, but adorned with brilliant flashes of colour when the fiddler crabs with their bright red or orange nippers move over the surface. These nippers are the fiddler crab's most characteristic feature; they are confined to the males and one only is enlarged; it may

PLATE 17.

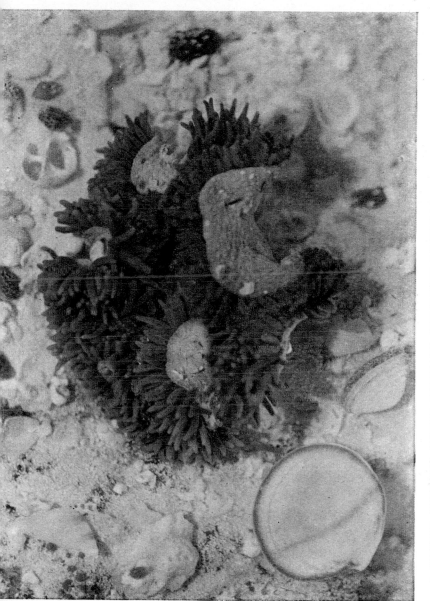

A PURPLE ANEMONE WHOSE DELICATE TENTACLES RESEMBLE THE PETALS OF A FLOWER

be larger than the rest of the crab's body. The movements of this great claw have been variously interpreted; by some they have been likened to a fiddler drawing his bow across the strings of a violin, by others they have been described as beckoning—beckoning perhaps to the females to come and share their homes. They are formidable and awesome weapons, and whether or not use is made of their ostentatious display to excite the admiration of the females, who, indeed, may well admire them for both their own claws are small and unadorned, they are certainly used as warnings to intruders when the crabs keep sentinel at the mouths of their burrows, and they are an effective fighting weapon when two males dispute the ownership of a grazing-ground or fight for the possession of a female which both have simultaneously viewed with amorous eyes. Approaching each other stealthily, like wrestlers searching for a grip, they suddenly rush together in a clinch, the great claws locking while the opponents heave and thrust and froth at the mouth till eventually one of them cries enough and beats an ignominious retreat.

Feeding is accomplished by means of the smaller of the claws, which moves backwards and forwards in quick succession, scooping into the mouth the surface sand containing minute forms of both animal and vegetable life left by the tide. And here is where the female comes into her own—she has two hands to feed with, for the fighting claw of the male is of little use for the purpose.

If alarmed the fiddler quickly makes for the protection of its burrow, which it may hastily descend, or it may remain just within the entrance with its great claw thrust out, for it seems to place great store on the devastating effect it will have on the courage of its aggressors. The burrows descend more or less vertically for two feet or more and they usually contain an inch or two of water at the bottom.

G

ROCK CRABS

There is still a third zone that maintains its distinctive crab life—the areas of rock lining the foreshores of many coral islands. Turn over one of the boulders and crabs will scamper into the nearest crevice or, if none is near, will back against the rock and with claws opened to their fullest extent and with nippers widespread defy your closer approach. Some of these crabs are of very pleasing colour and many are beautifully mottled (Plate 34, fig. 2). A common form, which may grow to a fairly large size, is mottled with green and fawn, and although preferring the shelter of rocks is capable of swimming freely; another prevalent type, but smaller in size, varies from brown to a pale slaty-blue; it is finely spotted and its eyes are a bright scarlet; and there are many others, for the most part small and inconspicuous.

Before we explore the reef, where we shall find many crabs of extraordinary interest, it is advisable that we learn something more about their mode of life and habits generally in order that we may the better understand the significance of much we have to describe.

HABITS OF CRABS

The crab grows by a series of moults. Its external covering is hard, unyielding, and incapable of further growth, and when the time comes for it to increase its size, when its rigid covering gives rise to "growing pains," the shell splits across the hinder end and the crab crawls out backwards, leaving behind not only the external shell but the hard lining of its stomach and part of its intestine. This is now the most critical period of the crab's existence, for it is soft and vulnerable, and it therefore crawls away and hides till a new shell develops. The animal continues to expand for some time after moulting, mainly by the absorption of water, and in the course of two or three days a new shell is deposited over its surface. It has been said that moulting is the price the crab pays for its protective armour, but it may at times be a distinct advantage, for the shells of older crabs may frequently have attached to them oysters, mussels, barnacles, tube worms, and other sedentary forms of life that have found the hard surface a convenient place to set up house. No doubt they enjoy their ride immensely for they are carried about from one feeding-ground to another, but as they grow they become a great encumbrance to the crab, till eventually it quits by the back entrance, leaving the menagerie stranded.

The frequency of moulting varies in different species, but in those crabs in which it has been investigated it has been found to occur more often than was originally suspected. For instance, an English shore crab was found to moult seventeen times in three years, and an American species moulted fifteen times during the first seven months of its existence and at the end of that time had attained a width of seven inches. The period between moults increases with age and moulting may eventually cease altogether.

Crabs hunt by scent rather than vision, and their feeding is a complicated process. Before the food enters the mouth it is manipulated by seven different pairs of appendages, beginning with the nippers or "hands" and eventually reaching the jaws which give it a preliminary crushing. A further pounding is received when it reaches the stomach whose walls are hard and are provided with three teeth that work together to form an efficient grinding mill. Most crabs have one claw considerably larger than the other and, although all may not serve the same function, their close relatives, the lobsters, have been seen to hold their prey with the smaller claw and kill it by heavy poundings with the larger one, in defiance, of course, of all the ethics of modern pugilistic practice.

Crabs' claws are remarkably strong, and it has been shown that one claw may support a weight equal to thirty times the weight of the crab's body. For comparison it may be remarked that a man's right hand is capable of a pull equal to about only two-thirds of his own weight.

Many of the lower animals have the power of regenerating lost parts, and this extremely useful faculty is very well developed in the crabs and their allies. If you grasp a crab by a claw you will probably be left with the claw in your hand; if it digs its nippers into your flesh and you endeavour to shake it off you may see the crab hurled to the ground while the claw remains fast. Situated near the base of each appendage there is a definite breaking plane; the crab can snap the limb off there at will and bleeding is prevented by the contraction of a membrane at the extremity of the stump. A bud quickly develops at the surface of the scar and when the next moult occurs it expands to form a completely new limb, though several moults may ensue before it attains its normal size.

All crabs walk sideways. The legs of one side are used to push with and those of the other to pull; all do not exert a pressure at the same time but rather work alternately so that progression is smooth and not a series of jerks.

Those crabs that live above the shore-line are capable of scenting water and if placed on the ground up to two hundred yards away from the water will invariably make in the right direction even though their course may take them part of the way uphill. After rain, however, the moisture all round them causes this sense of direction to be lost.

The early development of crabs is a most complicated process and in most cases the youngest stages, which are free-

PLATE 18.

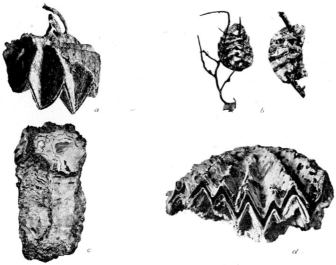

SOME REMARKABLE BARRIER REEF OYSTERS
a. Cockscomb oyster; *b.* leaf oysters; *c.* sea oyster, grown in an
overcrowded situation; *d.* giant oyster.

A SWIMMING MOLLUSC
The beautiful scarlet tentacles of this shellfish cannot be withdrawn into
the shell.

Photos: T. C. Roughley.

PLATE 19.

A BAILER SHELLFISH CRAWLING OVER THE SAND
Although the shell is as big as a football the great muscular foot is far
too large to be withdrawn into it.

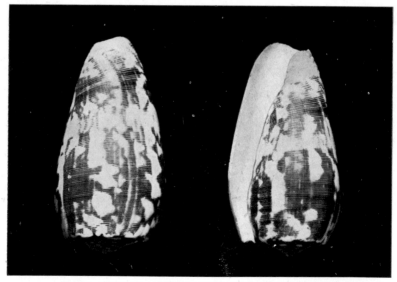

CONE SHELLS: UPPER AND LOWER SURFACES
These shellfish must be handled with great care for they can inflict a
dangerous wound.

Photos: T. C. Roughley.

swimming, for all crabs must breed in the sea, bear no resemblance to the parents, and it is not till after a series of moults that any sort of a likeness becomes apparent. But fascinating as this subject is we shall have to leave it and begin our wanderings over the reef in search of those curious creatures the observation of which has already been too long delayed.

HERMIT CRABS

As we roam amongst the coral our attention will probably be drawn to a shell that moves over the bottom at an uncommonly fast pace; realizing that all the shellfish we are familiar with crawl very slowly, our curiosity is aroused and, picking it up, we find that our shell contains, not a shellfish at all, but a crab—a hermit crab. Here is one of the most abundant and most interesting of all the crabs on the reef. Round some islands they are extraordinarily prolific. I was once collecting shells on a shore where they lay in millions about a foot deep near the water's edge, and leaving my collection on the sand above high-tide mark for about half an hour, I was astonished to find on my return that fully twenty per cent of them had crawled away. They were dead shells, but they formed the temporary abode of hermit crabs which had promptly crawled back to the moister region from which I had removed them.

Now, the hermit crab differs from all other crabs in the possession of an abdomen that is not covered by a hard shell like the front half of its body, and in order to protect this very vulnerable portion of its anatomy it requisitions the use of an empty shell into which it backs for protection (Plate 27, fig. 1). Long usage has adapted its body to the shells of sea-snails only, which are spirally wound, and the hinder portion of the body of the crab has taken on a similar curvature (Plate 28); near its extremity it is provided with a hook which it coils round the axis of the shell forming an attachment so secure that the crab cannot be removed without damage.

Like all other crabs, the hermit crab passes through a free-swimming stage, and when it has assumed the form of its parents it at once seeks a small shell for protection. But it must grow, and as it grows (by moulting, of course) it no longer fits the shell, and it is therefore forced to find another, a larger one. It never leaves its old home till it has found the new, and then it has to determine whether it is of the right size; this it appears to do by testing the entrance with its claws, and having decided that the fit is approximately correct it inserts its abdomen and backs in, the large and formidable claw effectively blocking the entrance. Moving day is always an anxious period in the life of the crab for shells of assorted sizes, particularly outsizes demanded by the larger individuals, are not displayed like shoes on a shelf for its choice. In his inimitable way Banfield pictures such an experience in the life of a hermit crab in these words:

"Disconsolate is the condition of the hermit crab who has outgrown his quarters, or has been enticed from them or 'drawn' by a cousin stronger than he, or who has had the fortune to be ejected without dismemberment. The full face of the red blue-spotted variety is an effective menace to any ordinary foe, and that honourable part is presented at the front door when the tenant is at home. For safety's sake the flabby, gelatinous, inert rear must be tucked and hooked into the convolutions of the shell, deprived of which he is at the mercy of foes very much his inferior in fighting weight and truculent appearance. The disinterested spectator may smile at the vain, yet frantically serious, efforts of the hermit to coax his flabby rear into a shell obviously a flattering misfit. But it is not a smiling matter for him. Not until he has

exhausted a programme of ingenious attitudes and comic con-
tortions is the attempt to stow away a No. 8 tail into a No. 5
shell abandoned. When a shell of respectable dimensions is
presented, and the grateful hermit backs in, settles comfort-
ably, arrays all his weapons against intruders, and peers out
with an expression of ferocious content, smiles may come, and
will be out of place only when the aches of still increasing
bulk force him to hustle again for still more commodious
lodgings."

One of the commonest—and the largest—of the hermit
crabs of the Great Barrier Reef is bright red with white or
bluish-white spots on its body; this is illustrated in a false
helmet shell in Plate 27, fig. 1, and a larger individual of
the same species which was removed from a bailer-shell is
shown in Plate 28. This is the species referred to above by
Banfield.

A close relative of the hermit crab is the famous robber
crab, an inhabitant of many coral islands in the Indian and
Pacific oceans, and, although it is not found on the Great
Barrier Reef it is of such peculiar interest that we may be
pardoned for digressing a moment to tell something of its
habits. The robber crab is a regular giant of its tribe and
may grow to a length of eighteen inches; its wanderings are
confined almost solely to the land, and it feeds on coco-nuts
which it obtains by climbing palms as high as sixty feet.
After cleaning off the fibrous outer covering the crab ham-
mers and tears at the "eye" with its powerful claws, and having effected an entrance it scrapes away the internal softer
part with its thinner hind legs. It has been recorded that
the natives of some of the islands, when they locate a crab in
a coco-nut palm, climb up some distance and fasten a girdle
of grass round the tree; the crab crawling down backwards
feels the grass beneath it and assuming that it has reached

the ground promptly lets go, to crash to the ground below, when it is either killed or badly stunned and is pounced upon by the natives. But if only partially stunned the larger crabs are handled with extreme caution for their great nippers can take a finger off with ease.

Although an offshoot from the hermit crabs, the robber crab no longer seeks to protect its abdomen in shells, and consequently its upper surface has again developed a hard covering (and, incidentally, lost its twist), but its lower surface remains soft and vulnerable, and if attacked the crab will thrust its abdomen into logs or holes to protect it. The gill cavities are greatly enlarged and are lined by spongy tissue richly supplied with blood-vessels that are capable of absorbing oxygen from the air. It must visit the sea, however, to hatch off the eggs.

ASSOCIATION OF CRABS WITH ANEMONES

It might well be assumed that the hard shells which hermit crabs choose to protect their soft parts would form a complete protection against any adversary, but there are some fishes, such as the eagle ray and the oyster-crusher, whose hard and powerful jaws are capable of crushing them with ease, and as a further protection it is not uncommon to find an anemone or several anemones perched on the outside of the hermit crab's shell (Plate 27, fig. 2). Now, these anemones can inflict very painful wounds by shooting out great quantities of poisonous darts, and they are therefore avoided by most other animals of the reef. Both the crab and the anemone benefit by this association, for the anemone comes in for the scraps that scatter about as the crab tears its prey to pieces, and the crab is afforded wonderful protection with a battery of machine-guns on its back.

An even stranger association between a crab and an anemone has been recorded from the Indian Ocean, for in this case the anemone is luminous and so provides the hermit crab with a living torch.

There are some free-living crabs on the reef, however, which are frequently found with anemones attached direct to their shells. The method of attachment adopted by the anemone is very interesting, for it turns upside-down, and as soon as the leg of a crab comes in contact with it, it folds itself about the limb and then works its way up to the crab's back.

But this is by no means the most extraordinary of such associations for another crab of the Indian Ocean habitually carries a stinging anemone in each claw and on the approach of an enemy waves them in its face. Not satisfied with this the crab gathers most of its food from the anemone's tentacles which stun their prey and then pass it from one to the other towards the mouth. The crab keeps its eye on the banquet table and whenever it sees a morsel that appeals to its palate it lifts up its second legs and calmly picks it off. This seems rather an ungrateful return for the protective assistance afforded by the anemone, but though its overhead costs are high and the leakages very heavy it probably profits by the increased turnover, for it is carried to where food is plentiful and so obtains as much or more than it would if left to remain in the one spot all its life.

SPIDER CRABS

During the world war the benefit derived from camouflaging the various instruments of warfare were found to be very great. A great gun, for instance, with a long steel barrel could be seen and recognized far off, and its contour was therefore broken up by weird designs painted on its surface in an endeavour to make it fit into its surroundings; machineguns were covered with bushes; and the uniforms of the soldiers themselves were of a colour that afforded them the maximum of concealment. In the eternal warfare of the reef many animals have developed by natural selection through the ages wonderfully protective coloration and markings which so blend with their surroundings that their recognition as animals is extremely difficult. The spider crabs and their allies, however, with their long, spindly legs have not been so fortunate in their development, and so they decorate themselves in the most extraordinary fashion with seaweed, sponges, and other forms of life common in the region where they live, until their characteristic crab *facies* is completely obliterated.

Although these crabs abound throughout the length and breadth of the reef, the visitor might spend months there without recognizing one, to such a degree of efficiency has their protective art been developed.

If nature has been neglectful in providing these crabs with protective markings it has been extremely generous in the provision of the means, and the development of a powerful instinct, which enable the crabs to effect their own disguises. They are masters in the art of make-up. Their nippers are very effective cutting tools; their backs and legs are covered with stout hooked hairs capable of holding securely such objects as are placed upon them; and the last pair of legs, or in some the last two pairs of legs, are turned up over the back in a handy position to manipulate the plant and animal life it desires to cultivate on its roof. Wandering about amongst the natural gardens of the reef, the crab nips off pieces of seaweed, sponges, and the like which it attaches to the hooked hairs on its back and limbs. The work is usually done with great discrimination in order that the garden may be in keeping, both in form and colour, with the dominant kinds of life that occur in the region of the crab's activities.

The growth of the cultivated garden is usually rapid and

it may eventually become a miniature forest. If, however, it spreads beyond the edges of the shell the crab carefully trims off the irregularities. A time is sometimes reached when the growth becomes so dense as to be an encumbrance, but it must be tolerated till the next moult is due when the crab slips away from under it to develop a fresh shell ready for the planting of another crop. This it at once proceeds to do and frequently picks over the growths on the old shell for the purpose.

The backs of some species are not provided with hairs, but, not to be outdone, they conceal themselves just as effectively (at least from above) by carrying a sponge or shell held permanently above them. If the sponge is too large the crab will remove it, trim it to the required size, and then replace it.

That considerable discrimination is shown by the crab in the course of its gardening activities has been demonstrated by placing one whose body was covered with seaweed in an aquarium amongst sponges; the crab at once set about divesting its back of the seaweed and redecorating it with the sponges.

One of the spider crabs of the Great Barrier Reef is invariably found in association with a seaweed known as *Halimeda*, the fronds of which are peculiarly flattened, and the shell of the crab assumes exactly the same shape and colour with the result that it can be distinguished only with great difficulty.

The spider crabs of the Great Barrier Reef are all small creatures and never attain a width beyond a few inches, but a giant of the tribe occurs in Japanese waters; it may measure up to twelve feet across the outstretched limbs. This is the world's largest crab; but a much bulkier one (which, however, is not a spider crab) occurs in the waters of Bass

Strait, between Australia and Tasmania. This giant crab may measure up to sixteen inches across the shell and may attain a weight of thirty pounds. It is considered that its nippers would be capable of breaking a man's wrist.

A GALL-FORMING CRAB

An entirely different form of protection is adopted by the gall-forming crab. It deliberately imprisons itself within the branches of coral! When still very young it takes up its position in the depression formed by a coral about to branch and in some mysterious way controls and alters the growth of the branches so that they broaden and later meet above to enclose the crab in a pocket or "gall," though small openings are always left between the branches to enable the water to circulate through it and bring to the crab the minute forms of animal and vegetable life upon which it feeds.

Now, these galls are inhabited by females only; the males, which are invariably much smaller, remain free-living throughout life. Before the tips of the branches fuse the male visits the female (no doubt to see that she is quite comfortable) and the young crabs eventually escape through the small apertures in the side of the prison. Although forced to lead a lonely and solitary life the female is afforded secure protection from her enemies, while the male fights the battles of the world unaided. How can we account for this extraordinary adaptation? Is it the selfishness of the female that impels her, with no thought of the risks run by her mate, to seek the protection of a buttressed castle, or is it the cunning of the male that encourages her to lock herself away from the world while he is free to stray unhampered by a nagging wife and unencumbered by family ties? The reader is left to form his own conclusions.

PLATE 20.

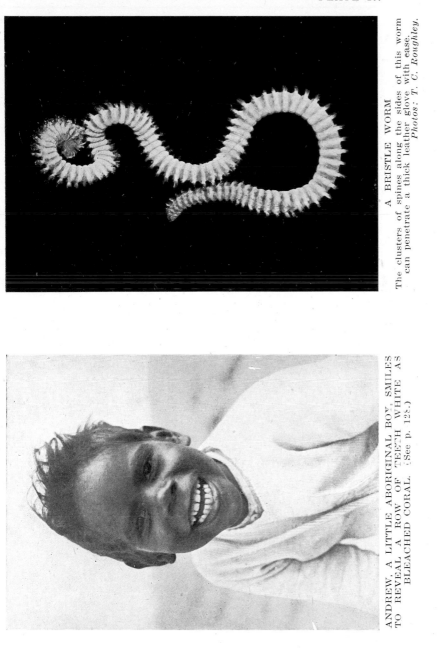

A BRISTLE WORM

The clusters of spines along the sides of this worm
can penetrate a thick leather glove with ease.

Photos: T. C. Roughley.

ANDREW, A LITTLE ABORIGINAL BOY, SMILES
TO REVEAL A ROW OF TEETH WHITE AS
BLEACHED CORAL. (See p. 128.)

PLATE 21.

THE SUCKER ON THE UPPER SURFACE OF THE
HEAD OF THE SUCKER-FISH
Photo: T. C. Roughley.

THE REPULSIVE AND POISONOUS STONE-FISH
IN A CORAL POOL
Photo: A. R. McCulloch.

A BOX CRAB

Another crab which is fairly prevalent but rarely seen burrows just beneath the surface of the sand and uses its stalked eyes as periscopes. If you dig it up and place it back on the sand it will sidle away a short distance and, facing you, will disappear beneath the surface in an instant, or, at least, all but its eyes will. Its nippers are of great size for so small a crab and when handled it folds them flat across the front giving it the appearance of a square box from which it has received the name of "box crab."

A CRAB THAT FEIGNS DEATH

A crab that is easily overlooked hides away during the daytime under coral boulders. If you turn one of these over you might be pardoned for imagining that, when all the other active creatures that it concealed had crawled or hopped away, the few large pebbles that remained were not worth a second glance. But pick one up and examine it carefully and you may find that it is a small crab with its nippers and legs drawn tightly to its body. It is shamming death. And this is its customary method of avoiding suspicion; it may lie like that without the slightest tremor for many minutes at a stretch.

PEA CRAB

And then there is the pea crab, a small creature with a soft but tough shell with all its edges smooth and rounded; it is frequently found inside the shells of live clams, fan shells, pearl-shells, and one or two species of oysters. Taking up its position on the gills of the animal whose sanctuary it has invaded it picks off the food which the mollusc is gathering and directing towards its mouth. One would imagine that its host would accordingly starve, but it does not appear to be affected detrimentally, and it is possible that the crab chooses only the larger particles which would probably be discarded by the mollusc in any case. The diminutive male wanders into the shell occasionally just to remind his larger mistress (one of several he visits) that he has not forgotten her.

THE SARGASSO OR WANDERING CRAB

At times, particularly after heavy seas, a small crab which is strictly not an inhabitant of the reef at all, may be found washed up on the beach. It is known as the wanderer crab because of its habit of attaching itself to pieces of seaweed, wood, and other flotsam and jetsam, which carry it about over the ocean at the mercy of wind and current. This is the crab that Columbus found in the Sargasso Sea and it served to convince his sailors that land was near at hand, which, of course, was not necessarily the case. From its frequent occurrence in those waters the crab is usually referred to as the Sargasso crab.

SWIMMING CRABS

Several kinds of Barrier Reef crabs can swim actively by means of the paddle-like formation of the last pair of legs. Two species are very common; they grow to a large size and are delicious to eat. One of them, the giant mangrove swimming crab, makes great burrows in the sand or in broken coral usually in the vicinity of mangroves, where the holes may be seen up to a foot or more in diameter, and on the mainland coast it is a pest to the oyster cultivator, for its great powerful nippers are capable of crushing the shells of fairly large oysters, and they could probably break a man's finger.

The attraction of the crabs of the Barrier is by no means confined to their curious habits, however, for many of them are very beautiful. Two species commonly found amongst the coral are illustrated in Plate 33, figs 1 and 2. The uppermost of these is extremely abundant amongst the branches of

staghorn coral, and in the Capricorn Group, at least, specimens may be found in nearly every bunch that is broken off
and brought ashore, for they remain amongst the branches
when they are removed from the water. Its great cumbersome nippers are much heavier than the whole of the rest of
its body.

One of the most striking of reef crabs is that known as the
barometer crab. It has derived its name from the belief that
the density of the large blood-red spots on the surface of
the shell alters with the state of the weather. There are
eleven of these spots symmetrically arranged on a delicate
lilac ground; four of them are disposed along the hinder part
of the shell, three in close apposition across the middle, and
two pairs on the front edge external to the eyes.

AN ENEMY OF CRABS

In view of the extraordinary precautions taken by crabs to
protect their bodies which, on account of their hardness, would
appear to offer little attraction as a diet, we are forced to the
assumption that other creatures besides man find their flesh
uncommonly palatable. Their greatest enemy is the octopus.
Lurking in crevices this sly and crafty creature waits patiently
for a crab to pass his way; a long arm shoots out and the
struggling crab, stuck fast to the suckers that stud its lower
surface, is dragged into the den. I have several times wit-
nessed fights between octopuses and crabs and, although the
octopus always won, I was never able to determine by what
means it killed its adversary. It has a beak, certainly, but
this is not a very formidable weapon, and it was always impossible to decide whether the suckers played any important
part in the combat, but there appears to be considerable evidence to indicate that the octopus paralyses the crab by inject-

ing beneath its shell a poisonous substance secreted by its salivary glands.

AN INSIDIOUS PARASITE OF CRABS

But some of the crabs of the reef have a more insidious enemy, and curiously enough it is one of the crab's distant relatives. A small crustacean, after undergoing a series of transformations characteristic of the race generally, attaches itself to a crab and immediately begins to bore a hole through the shell; having accomplished this the contents of its body pass into the interior of the crab and the external skeleton falls away. The portion that has passed into the crab is carried in the blood-stream and attaches itself to the intestine where it sends out roots which gradually penetrate every part of the crab's body. Meanwhile, the central mass works towards the under side of the crab and during the following moult pushes its way through to form a large sac containing the reproductive elements.

Crabs infected by this parasite, which is known as *Sacculina,* do not again moult, and although females show little external change, the males may take on all the characters of females.

THE "PAINTED" LOBSTER

Of all the crab's relatives on the reef the lobster is the largest and most conspicuous; so gaudily marked is it that it is usually referred to as the "painted" lobster, but its colour is so variable that a detailed description is rendered impracticable. It displays a wonderful blend of blue, mauve, purple, green, orange, brown, red, and black, broken by spots on various parts of its body and stripes along the legs. This lobster is in places very common, but it is rarely seen abroad during the daytime for it hides in crevices amongst the coral at the edges of pools and is usually only betrayed by the long

PLATE 22.

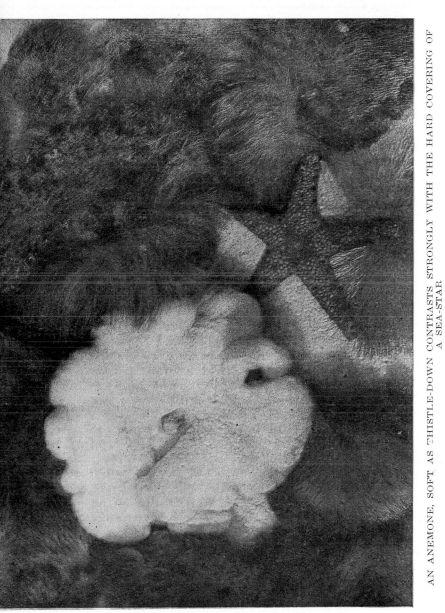

AN ANEMONE, SOFT AS THISTLE-DOWN CONTRASTS STRONGLY WITH THE HARD COVERING OF
A SEA-STAR

antennae jutting out from its hiding-place. As many as half a dozen may sometimes be taken from one small pool. It grows to a length of about sixteen inches and is excellent eating.

THE MANTIS SHRIMP

Another of the crab's interesting relatives is the mantis prawn or mantis shrimp as it is just as frequently called (Plate 25, fig. 1). This fierce and active creature has derived its name from the resemblance of its claws and the manner of their use to those of the devout but hypocritical praying mantis of our bush. It grows to a length of about nine inches, although some species are much smaller, and lives in holes it constructs in the sand or in crevices amongst the coral. The colour of the numerous species varies greatly; most of those seen darting about in the daytime are drab brown or black, but others may be found of great beauty, the body varying from a pale cinnamon to a moss-green, soft and pleasing, or it may be mottled and spotted (as in the specimen illustrated) with a variety of delicate colours, while the two enlarged and opposed portions of the nippers may be very brilliant; in one species the last segment of these is a bright vermilion and the second last a rich blue. The claws fold together like the blades of a pocket-knife; in some species they terminate in needle-like points curved inwards, while in others they are armed along their opposing edges with long, curved, and sharp teeth.

These claws or nippers are used for catching their prey. They strike with lightning-like rapidity and their power is remarkable. Once when I was about to photograph a six-inch specimen in a dish of water I touched the front of it with a glass rod in order to alter its position and it promptly knocked the rod out of my hand; and it has been known, when dropped into a glass tube filled with alcohol, to shatter

H

the tube with a blow. If handled it can inflict a nasty wound, and in Bermuda and the West Indies the reputation it has established for itself has been responsible for its name of "split thumb." But even if it were perfectly harmless it would be extremely difficult to catch, for at your approach it darts away in a zigzag course with great speed and disappears into a burrow or into the coral like a flash.

The food of the mantis shrimp consists of live fish and prawns (it is known to New South Wales fishermen as "prawn-killer"), and it is very partial to newly-moulted crabs. It usually lies inside the mouth of its burrow with its head and claws projecting, ready in an instant to grab an unwary victim.

In most crabs and their allies the plume-like feet attached to the abdomen are used principally for the securing of the eggs, but in the mantis shrimp they are adapted to serve the purpose of gills.

THE NOISY NIPPER PRAWN

When walking in shallow water, particularly in muddy areas, one's attention is frequently attracted by sharp reports that sound like huge crabs snapping their claws together or perhaps crushing shellfish. The source of the sound is usually very difficult to locate because the creature responsible for it is quite a small prawn, known as an Alpheid or more commonly as a "nipper" prawn, which although small has one of its claws developed into a large and bulky structure, and its custom of snapping its fingers together sharply causes a loud report, which continually breaks the silence of the swamp.

BARNACLES

Probably the most curious of all the crab's relatives, though from its garb and posture it does not appear at first sight to be even remotely related to it, is the barnacle. Attached to rocks and covered with shelly plates, it bears a far closer resemblance to a shellfish for which it is very frequently mistaken, but its internal anatomy and its development disclose its relationship to the crab.

The cone-shaped barnacle that attaches itself to stones along the foreshores does not appear to be common anywhere throughout the extent of the reef, but the stalked or goose barnacle is frequently washed ashore attached to driftwood. The tough brown stalks may be a foot or more long and the bodies of the barnacles at their extremities are encased in flattened shelly plates of a delicate pale blue colour. As the plates open, the animal thrusts out a series of curved limbs that serve to collect the food, and they have been described as kicking the food into the mouth.

The term "goose" barnacle has been derived from the idea prevalent in England from the twelfth to the seventeenth century that migratory birds that reach the English coast from arctic regions in the autumn developed from these barnacles, and this theory no doubt had its origin in the simultaneous appearance of the birds and the barnacles, the latter being frequently washed ashore during the gales common in the autumn. Late in the seventeenth century the "birds" enclosed within the shells of the barnacles were described in a paper read before the Royal Society of London!

CHAPTER	*Shellfish of Great*
TEN	*Beauty and Interest*

THE Great Barrier Reef is a region of extremes. Animal life of indescribable beauty mingles with forms that are ugly and repulsive; great giants lie side by side with their diminutive relatives; and boldness and ferocity contrast strangely with extreme delicacy and sensitiveness.

For beauty and delicacy of colour, for attractiveness of design and pattern, the shellfish life of the Barrier is surpassed only by the fishes that swim lazily in the coral pools. The shells are almost infinite in their variety, and round some of the islands they are to be found washed up on the beaches in enormous quantities. The decorative qualities of many of them have for a long period of years led to their extensive display in homes and gardens for ornamental purposes. The shells of large cowries, beautifully spotted or striped and richly glazed; spider-shells with their long "arms" and rich shade of pink; the frail and delicately sculptured paper nautilus; and a host of others have decorated mantelpieces and cabinets in thousands of homes, while the great shells of the giant clam have found a niche amongst the shrubbery of many gardens.

But these are the shells, the skeletons, of the animals; their interest lies in their intrinsic beauty only, and even that is often surpassed by the beauty of the animals that once inhabited them, while the habits of the animals responsible for their construction have a far deeper interest. These can be studied only by visiting the reef.

PLATE 23.

LIKE A DELICATE FLOWER THIS SMALL ANEMONE SPREADS ITS TENTACLES IN A GARDEN OF CORAL AND SEAWEEDS

To one who has been accustomed to gathering shells washed up on the beaches in more sober regions the first encounter with the giant clam of the Barrier Reef causes a momentary shock; to one who has been used to scooping up shells in handfuls, a pair of shells that it would take four or five persons to lift cannot fail to evoke expressions of amazement.

THE GIANT CLAM

The giant clam is widely distributed throughout the northern half of the reef; it is probably most abundant along the inner side of the outer barrier and may occur beyond it to a depth of several fathoms. In the southern area of the reef it does not occur at all, its place being taken by a smaller but much more brilliant species. The giant clam is easily the largest shellfish in the world; it is commonly seen up to a length of three feet and may grow to four feet six inches with a weight of four or five hundredweight; at least authentic records of shells that size have been obtained, but divers have reported seeing shells far larger in the deeper water.

The giant clam is common on reefs in shallow water, and during very low spring tides the edges of the shells of numbers of them may be uncovered for short periods. Unlike many of its smaller relatives, which are securely attached, the giant clam simply rests on the bottom with the hinge side downwards, and when the shells gape each valve displays along its inner border a wide expanse of mantle. This mantle is responsible for the secretion of the shell, and although in the giant clam it is never brilliantly coloured its velvety consistency in shades of brown or olive green with darker transverse markings and bright green spots gives it a richness that is very pleasing.

When the shells are gaping widely two prominent circular openings can be seen lying in the tissue between the mantles; water is continually being drawn into one, and after the food it contains is sifted it passes out through the other. As the clams are uncovered during low spring tides they will frequently be seen to squirt columns of water into the air to clear themselves of accumulated sediment and waste food matter which might cause irritation to the animal during the hours of enforced closure.

The food of the clam consists of the same microscopic forms of life as those upon which the oyster, mussel, and other bivalves feed, but unlike its smaller relatives it has a supplementary source of supply—it cultivates a vegetable garden in its tissues. We have seen that reef-building corals contain great quantities of extremely small plant-cells that are continually making oxygen available to the polyps and absorbing the carbon dioxide which they in turn give off as a waste product. Somewhat similar plant cells are found abundantly distributed throughout the surface layers of the clam's mantle, but here they appear to have an additional function; their ranks are continually being drawn upon to augment the clam's normal food-supply.

The mantle is of very tough consistency and if touched it is withdrawn, sometimes slowly, sometimes rapidly, within the shells which close over it. The two valves of the shell are pulled together by a centrally situated adductor muscle which may measure up to six inches in diameter; with a direct pull between the two valves the power of this muscle is enormous, and naked divers are reputed to have been trapped by inadvertently placing a foot between the wide-open shells which, closing together, have gripped them as in a vice. This, of course, is quite possible, for the power of man is far too inadequate to enable him to force the shells apart unaided by a crowbar or other similar implement. There is no risk of being trapped by a shell that is growing in an isolated situation; it is far too conspicuous an object for that; but the identity of older specimens may be lost when covered by an abundance of marine growths and by corals growing up about them, and then with a gape that may extend up to twelve inches in width, it is certainly possible for a barefooted native to insert his foot between the valves of the shell and for the closing valves to grip his foot before he has a chance to withdraw it. But the chances against all these conditions occurring at the one time are so great that I cannot help thinking that the number of fatalities caused by their agency has been greatly exaggerated.

The flesh of giant clams is not relished by white people, but it is occasionally eaten by the blacks, the great adductor muscle being the portion most sought after. Before the advent of whites the shells were used extensively by the natives on the waterless islands of the reef and Torres Strait to hold and store fresh water during heavy rains; they were placed under Pandanus-trees, and long strips of bark were tied round the trunks and suspended into the upturned shells thus serving to conduct the water to the basin-like containers.

Occurring in similar situations the horse-shoe clam is found in even greater abundance. This clam never grows to the great size of its relative, for it is rarely found more than a foot long, but it is relatively wider and is the most conspicuous object to be found on many of the reefs. Its mantle edges are always a dull green, and like the giant clam it is never attached.

BURROWING CLAMS

Although less conspicuous on account of their relatively small size, the burrowing clams occur in far greater numbers than either of those just described. The species that inhabit the northern half of the reef burrow into dead coral of the more solid types and into coral rock, and each boulder over a wide area may have dozens showing at the surface. How can we account for these clams, covered by hard shells and with no special boring apparatus, being embedded in solid rock? In their earliest stages of growth they are free-swimming and on completion of this roving life they settle on the hard surface of the coral, search for a depression or crevice, and then attach themselves by secreting strong threads through an opening that remains permanent at the hinge end of the shell; shortly after settling down they rock themselves to and fro in the direction of the long axis of the shell, and gradually wear away the coral stone beneath them. As they grow they penetrate deeper and deeper and when about an inch long the external edges of their shells lie flush with the surface; but the rocking must continue throughout the life of the animal to maintain the cavity large enough for the increasing growth of the shell. The boring movement is a very restricted one and, consequently, there is very little space between the shells and the rock in which they have formed a pocket. These clams grow to a length of about six inches.

In the southern half of the reef the most brilliant, the most beautiful of all clams occur. Unlike the giant clam they are always attached at the hinge end by means of a solid fleshy stalk that projects through the shell. Their numbers are legion; indeed, it is almost impossible to stand on the coral anywhere without some of them being in view, and in some places dozens may be seen in an area of twenty square yards.

And their colours! The brilliance and richness of their

mantles are rivalled only by their variety (Plates 36 and 37). Bright purples, blues, and greens mingle with the more sober browns, fawns, and greys, or the mantles may display a combination of any two of those colours, mottled, banded, or striped; indeed, the colour combinations are limitless and I have never seen two mantles exactly alike, but red is the one colour never seen. Lying just beneath the surface of the crystal clear water with the sun shining full upon them the more showy mantles glisten and sparkle, while those of softer hue resemble the richest of velvet. Nature was in her most lavish mood when she filled her palette to adorn these clams; nature alone could display such brilliance, for the colours live.

These clams never exceed a length of more than about twelve inches.

The boring of clams into dead coral tends always to undermine it and to help in its decay. Each year sees its crop of young clams ready to begin their boring activities, but this work of destruction is by no means confined to the clams, for even amongst their bivalve relatives there are others equally destructive. Chief amongst them is the date mussel which, although smaller than any of the clams, does not confine its activities to the surface, but continues its tunnel till the animal may lie several inches within the rock. It bores in a very different way, however, for the action is not mechanical but chemical; a special gland secretes an acid which eats away the limestone. Now, it would be futile for the clam to attempt to burrow by this means, even if it were capable of secreting acid, for the surface of its shell would be just as susceptible to its action, but the shell of the date mussel is lined externally with a layer that is acid-resisting.

EDIBLE OYSTERS

There would not appear to be much scope for the production of striking varieties of the edible oyster, but even with these shells, which are usually most uninteresting (until opened, of course), the Barrier Reef has produced some surprises. A Roman Emperor, Aulus Vitellius, who reigned during the first century of the Christian era (and who, by the way, should be the patron saint of all oyster-growers), is reputed to have consumed a hundred dozen oysters at one sitting. If this gourmand had lived on the Barrier Reef he (or his staff) would have been saved much time and labour opening them, for he could have partaken of oysters weighing up to seven pounds! This is the world's largest oyster (Plate 18, fig. 1*d*), and a dozen of them would, I should imagine, test even Vitellius's powers of gastronomic endurance! Like many other species of bivalves that grow in situations where violent wave action is likely to place a great strain on the valves of the shell, it is characterized by sharply scalloped edges which so securely interlock that effective lateral resistance is provided against the heaviest of seas.

This deep scalloping of the edges is seen at its greatest development in the oyster illustrated in fig. 1*a* of the same plate; to such a degree has it been carried that it no longer appears like an oyster at all; its deeply indented contour resembles rather the comb of a rooster and, in consequence, it is usually referred to as the "cockscomb" oyster. As the specimen in the illustration shows, it may sometimes have long extensions of the shell growing from its surface, but just what purpose they serve it is impossible to say.

Even more curious are the oysters illustrated in fig. 1*b* of Plate 18. From the lower valve curved finger-like projections grow out to envelop branches of black horny coral, but the attachment is rarely, if ever, a rigid one for the oyster can be moved around the branch with freedom. Just how this oyster secures a hold initially is not known with certainty, but it is probable, I think, that attachment in the first place is accomplished in the normal manner by cementing the shell to the coral and the projections of the shell are secreted round the branch at a later date. It is an extraordinary provision to maintain the shell in contact with the branch, for, on account of its narrowness and flexibility no oyster growing to that size could adhere to such a limited surface if the ordinary means of attachment alone were available to it.

It is scarcely to be credited that the specimen illustrated in Plate 18, fig. 1c is an oyster, yet it is a true edible oyster that has grown in a densely over-crowded situation. Normally, when allowed to grow unrestricted by pressure from its neighbours it assumes a more or less triangular shape, but if contact with those about it prevents further growth of the shell along the rock it is forced to grow upwards away from it till it may assume the greatly elongated shape of the specimen illustrated. This appears to be a very slow-growing oyster for the shell is very dense, and if one may judge from the great length of the hinge-line, this particular specimen was a great age; just how old can only be conjectured, but I should imagine that it would be at least thirty years. With the exception of a cup-shaped depression beneath the upper valve or lid, which houses the soft parts of the oyster, the rest of the shell consists of solid limestone.

This is the most abundant and widely distributed oyster of the Great Barrier Reef. It grows in a well-defined zone situated between about mean low-water and mean high-water level, and when the crop is a heavy one it appears at low spring tides as a continuous band which may extend along the rocks for hundreds of yards. It will grow only in sea-water where the density remains uniformly high, and attempts that have been made to transfer it to estuarine waters where it would be amenable to cultivation have invariably ended in failure, for the first sign of a "fresh" is usually fatal to it. On account of the fact that its habitat is restricted to offshore waters it is usually referred to as the "sea oyster."

Concerning its flavour there is a diversity of opinion. It is many years ago that I first tasted it, when, landing at low tide on Ethel Rocks situated in the sea a few miles southeast of Gladstone, I found myself on a virgin bed of them; they smothered the rocks everywhere to the exclusion of almost all other forms of life. After making a careful survey and procuring specimens and photographs I felt free to sit down and indulge myself at their expense, but although the flesh was beautifully white and as attractive as any oyster I have ever seen, I found a certain tang in their flavour that did not appeal to my palate and, after eating two or three, I decided that after all it was scarcely fair to disturb the peace of such a happy and wellbred community.

The sea oyster is like a tropical fruit; to appreciate it one must acquire a taste for it, and judging by the favour in which it is held by those who have eaten it over a period of years, it apparently develops a palatableness which the mere tiro usually fails to appreciate.

Suspecting that the tang I noticed might be traceable to iodine, in which all oysters are extremely rich, averaging about two hundred times as much as milk, eggs, or beefsteak, I later had the iodine content determined and it proved to be twice as high as in any previously recorded species.

If you live in a "goitre belt" holiday on the Barrier Reef and eat plenty of sea oysters!

PLATE 24.

THIS LARGE BLUE SEA-STAR ABOUNDS THROUGHOUT THE BARRIER REEF
(One-half natural size.)

SWIMMING SHELLFISH

Although all shellfish begin their lives in a free-swimming condition, many of them after wandering about for a week or two settle down, lose their powers of locomotion, and never again alter their position; others retain a strong muscular organ or "foot" which they can thrust beyond their shells and by its extension and contraction move over the surface of the sand or plough their way through it; and yet a third type, such as the scallop, and a bivalve known as *Lima*, retain their swimming powers throughout life.

The symmetrical shells of the scallop, attractively sculptured and delicately tinted, are frequently found washed up on the beaches of Barrier Reef islands but the living animals are not often seen. They swim through the water, usually in a zigzag course, by a series of sudden contractions of the two valves of the shell which forcibly expel water in two narrow jets, one on each side of the hinge. The edges of the mantles are beset with a great number of large and prominent eyes constructed on the same general plan as the human eye but far less efficient.

Less active, but nevertheless capable of swimming with a jerky movement, is the beautiful bivalve *Lima* which is usually found hidden beneath coral boulders either on the reef flats or occasionally on the foreshore. The shell of this curious creature is smooth and white or creamy-white, and projecting from the edges of the mantles are many beautiful scarlet tentacles of great length which although highly contractile can never be withdrawn entirely into the shell (Plate 18, fig. 2). *Lima* also propels itself through the water by a sudden snapping together of the two valves of its shell, but it is by no means so accomplished a swimmer as the scallop.

TYPES OF SHELLFISH

Up to the present our observations have been confined to those shellfish that are enclosed or partially enclosed within a pair of valves and are therefore known as bivalves. But these form only one of several kinds of molluscs (as shellfish are more correctly termed) which the reader will find on the reef, and a word or two of explanation concerning the principal types he is likely to encounter will therefore not be out of place.

The shells of bivalves are secreted by the mantle which hangs usually as two flaps on the sides of the animal, and the more active kinds are provided with a tongue-like foot which is modified in various ways for creeping, digging, or jumping. The head is rudimentary and scarcely distinguishable as such, and the gills are usually in the form of two large flat plates covered with minute hairs which continually draw the water over them through the gaping valves of the shells. They also serve another and equally important function, that of collecting the minute particles of food suspended in the water and conveying them to the mouth. The opening of the valves of the shell is effected by an elastic ligament situated at the hinge; they are closed by one and sometimes two powerful muscles which extend from valve to valve internally. The power of these muscles is very great, and it has been found that each square centimetre of area exerts a pressure in the oyster of from thirteen to fourteen pounds, and in a bivalve known as *Venus* of as much as twenty-seven pounds.

An even more extensive group is that in which the animal is covered with a single spiral shell; these are known as univalves or Gastropods, and embrace such well-known shellfish as sea-snails, periwinkles, and whelks. Fundamentally their organization resembles that of the bivalves.

but there are several important modifications. For instance, the entrance to the shell is usually closed securely, when the animal withdraws into it, by means of a horny or shelly operculum or lid secreted by the tissues of the foot, which is flat and lies beneath the animal. The head is clearly differentiated from the rest of the body and is usually provided with eyes elevated by means of stalks. Most are furnished with a tongue-like strap known as a radula which is beset with numerous fine teeth arranged in transverse rows; this serves to break the food up as it passes along its surface. The teeth on the radula vary greatly in form, arrangement, and number; there may be as few as sixteen and as many as three-quarters of a million. The gills of Gastropods also differ from those of bivalves in their comb-like arrangement.

A third group that we shall meet extensively on the reef, the Loricates or Chitons, embrace a type of shellfish which is covered or partially covered, not by one or two shells, but by eight arranged along the middle line of the back. A fourth group we shall have to consider embraces curious molluscs known as sea-hares, which are not covered by a shell but carry it internally, while a fifth group known as Nudibranchs, or naked-gilled molluscs, never have a shell at all in the adult condition; and finally we shall have something to say about the most active and highly organized of all molluscs, the octopus and its allies.

THE BAILER-SHELL

One of the largest and most interesting of the univalves or Gastropods inhabiting the waters of the Great Barrier Reef is the bailer- or melon-shell, which is very common on the reef flats everywhere. It has received the former name because of its extensive use by the blacks as a bailer for their canoes, a purpose for which it is eminently adapted, and the latter from its resemblance both in shape and pattern to a water-melon. The shell of the bailer may grow to a length of about sixteen inches, and the animal may frequently be found partially buried in the sand through which it burrows by means of an enormous foot. This foot when fully extended may be almost twice the length of the shell and may attain a weight of several pounds (Plate 19, fig. 1). Projecting beyond the anterior edge of the shell a long trunk-like siphon remains always above the surface; its function is to draw a continual stream of water into the animal to bathe the gills.

The shell of the bailer is smooth and rounded externally, and the hinder end terminates in a spirally-arranged series of spines which increase in size as the spiral widens; it is cream or ochreous-yellow in colour, sometimes ornamented with two transverse bands of light brown. Internally the shell is a rich apricot. The great muscular foot varies in colour from black to a brown or greenish-brown flecked with irregular yellow spots; it is tough and rubbery, and, although the palates of white people find it rather tasteless, it was relished by the blacks who sometimes used the shell to boil the animal that made it. Boiled in its own skin, as it were. Indeed, the shell of the bailer was one of the most useful utensils available to these primitive people for they made it serve the purpose, according to Banfield, of a bucket, saucepan, drinking-vessel, basket and—wardrobe, though a wardrobe would scarcely seem of much value to them in their original uncivilized state; in any case the bailer-shell would surely be far too commodious for the purpose.

Spawning occurs during the summer months when the animal secretes a glistening white or yellow cone-shaped structure somewhat resembling a cob of corn in shape, and as

PLATE 25.

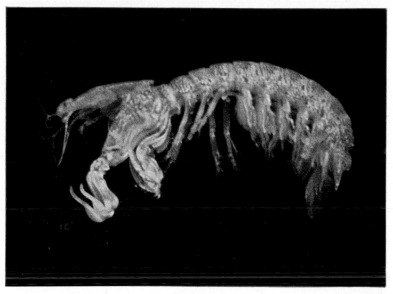

MANTIS SHRIMP
(Three-fifths natural size.)

SLATE-PENCIL SEA-URCHIN
(Two-fifths natural size.)

much as nine or ten inches long and two inches in diameter; capsules containing the developing young are arranged irregularly round a central hollow core, and when the baby bailers have grown to a length of about one and a quarter inches they break through to the channel in the middle and so reach the outside world. The shells of the newly-hatched young ones are white with brownish markings.

THE HELMET SHELL

Equally as large and far more bulky is the helmet or cameo shell which is widely distributed over the northern area of the Barrier. The massive shell bears a striking resemblance to the helmets worn by ancient warriors, and it has been carved (along with others from the Indian Ocean) to form the cameos of commerce.

CONE SHELLS

Everywhere over the reef flats cone shells are extremely abundant; they are usually about three to four inches long, and several species are highly poisonous. They are armed with a long fleshy proboscis which can be protruded well beyond the edge of the shell; this organ is provided with a number of sharp teeth each of which has a venom gland at the base; it is used normally to paralyse its prey, but if handled carelessly it is liable to be jabbed into the hand with results that may be serious; it is capable of causing a partial paralysis or even death. A fatality from this source occurred on one of the mainland islands in June 1935; a visitor was carrying one of the shells (Plate 19, fig. 2) when the proboscis pierced his hand; a little later symptoms of poisoning developed and he was rushed to the mainland, but died before reaching hospital.

Cone shells are prettily ornamented, mostly in wavy stripes, and the internal surface of the shell is usually bright

I

orange-red. If one is turned on its back a sickle-shaped projection from the foot is thrust out a distance about equal to the length of the shell, and with a broad, vigorous sweep downwards it is pushed into the sand to lever the shell over. A pair of eyes is situated at the extremities of long stalks, and each is beautifully marked with concentric bands of various colours.

THE SPIDER-SHELL

Another interesting shellfish which is common in similar situations is the spider-shell, the upper surface of which is usually dull and more or less eroded, but the lower surface is a most delicate pink. It has derived its name from the long, curved spines that project from the margin of the shell; these are usually about seven in number and some may attain a length equal to that of the shell itself.

BORERS OR DRILLS

The greatest enemies of shellfish, at least of the smaller kinds, are snail-like members of their own race provided with a boring apparatus with which they drill a small hole in the shell of their victim and then suck out the soft parts. Several species of these boring shellfish are common on the Barrier Reef, and, if one examines the shells washed up on the beach, quite a big proportion of them will frequently be found drilled with the characteristic small round hole. Drilling is accomplished by means of the radula, and it is probable that the boring is facilitated by the secretion of sulphuric acid which dissolves away the lime. In addition to these enemies, there are several species of fish, such as sting-rays and "oyster-crushers," that are capable of crushing quite hard shells.

In view of the depredations of these foes it is not surprising to find that many shellfish have adopted devices that have a protective value. The spines and deep furrows ornamenting many of them serve as a protection against the boring apparatus of their principal enemy by preventing it from obtaining a sufficient purchase to use it. There is one shellfish, however, that takes quite elaborate precautions to hide its shell; it is known as the carrier shell from its habit of carrying on its back numbers of other shells, pieces of coral or pebbles, which it cements to its shell by a special secretion, so that the animal is completely obscured by the miscellaneous collection of objects above it.

COWRIES

The most popular of all the shells of the Barrier Reef are undoubtedly the cowries, and probably more of these have been gathered as souvenirs than all the rest of the shells combined. The one most sought after is the tiger cowrie, though why it should be called "tiger" is difficult to imagine—probably because it is spotted to resemble very closely the skin of a leopard. The shell of this cowrie grows to a length of about four inches; it is one of the most beautiful of all shells, its rich glaze and rounded spots of dark brown or green with soft outlines, irregularly distributed over a ground colour of ivory white or the palest shade of brown or green, giving it a decorative quality and a peculiar charm that have fascinated shell collectors of all times.

When wandering over the reef these cowries are commonly picked up alive, the animal lying snug within the toothed aperture extending along the under side of the shell, but occasionally the shell will be found completely hidden by the paired mantles which are extended through the aperture and spread up over the shell till they meet in the middle line along the back (Plate 38, fig. 1). These mantle folds are beautifully mottled and are covered with long, bluntly-pointed tentacles. Tiger-cowries are usually found in pairs.

The Barrier Reef produces many other kinds of cowries with a wide range of patterns and colours, and all without exception are very beautiful; some resemble the richest of tortoise-shell, others are banded in the most delicate shades of brown, and others again may be as white as the finest porcelain; indeed, from these the term "porcelain" is reputed to have received its name. These pure white shells are used extensively by the natives of Torres Strait and New Guinea for the decoration of their canoes and for personal adornment.

Money cowries, so-called because until quite recently they were used as currency by certain West African tribes, are extremely abundant. They grow to a length of about one and a quarter inches and their subdued tones of cream, green, brown, or blue, with a faint suggestion of transverse bands and a narrow ring of orange on the surface of some, form a delicate and extremely pleasing combination that has given them a widespread popularity as playing-card counters.

In the daytime cowries usually remain concealed under stones or hidden away in crevices amongst the coral with their bodies completely withdrawn inside the shell, but at night they wander forth in search of food, when their richly coloured mantles are found displayed to their utmost. These mantles are responsible for the secretion of the shells, which retain their glaze and colour indefinitely.

It is quite common to find under upturned boulders cowries depositing great masses of eggs that glisten white or cream in the sunlight.

"CATS'-EYES"

Another favourite object that attracts collectors is the "cat's-eye," a disk-shaped shell with a central area of rich, deep green surrounded by a lighter band, part white, part brown. This is the operculum or lid by means of which the

PLATE 26.

A BÊCHE-DE-MER ENTANGLED IN STICKY THREADS WHICH IT
EJECTED WHEN IRRITATED

A GREEN TURTLE BASKING IN THE WARMTH OF A SHALLOW
POOL

turban shellfish closes the entrance to its shell when it withdraws into its interior. Cats'-eyes have been extensively employed for jewellery ornamentation, and the Maoris of New Zealand frequently used them as eyes for their idols.

MUTTON-FISH

Thus far we have been considering those shellfish which are capable of withdrawing their soft parts entirely within their shells, but there are some whose shells are so small that they are capable of enveloping a small part of the animal only, others which permanently carry their shells within their soft parts, and a further kind which, although belonging to the great group of shellfish, paradoxically have no shell at all.

A common example of the type of mollusc incapable of retracting entirely within its shell is the mutton-fish, which is widely distributed throughout the whole Barrier Reef area. The shell of the mutton-fish is generally known as an "ear-shell" on account of a fancied resemblance to that organ, and the commonest species on the reef has received the further designation of "ass's ear." It is roughly oval in shape and lies on the upper surface of the body covering portion only of the anterior half of the animal; near the left edge of the shell and running parallel with it is a series of apertures which decrease in size as they extend towards the spirally-wound apex where those which were formed earliest are usually found closed up (Plate 38, fig. 2); through these apertures the tentacles of the mantle are protruded. The portion of the animal not covered by the shell consists mainly of a large muscular foot, fringed above, and handsomely mottled with various shades of green on a pale cream ground. The animal is able to crawl about actively and when adherent to a flat stone the suction of the lower surface of its foot renders its removal difficult.

Internally the shell has a brilliant green and pink iridescence which has caused it to be used extensively as an inlay for ornamental purposes, and in the manufacture of buttons and jewellery.

The foot has a delicious flavour when boiled or fried, and is extensively eaten in various parts of the world. In California, where the animal is known as an abalone, there is a regular market for it, and in 1935 a beginning was made there to can the minced flesh and the broth. In England the shells are known both as ear-shells and ormers.

LORICATES

The members of another group of shellfish, known as Loricates, or perhaps more frequently as Chitons, are provided with eight shells that overlap along the middle line of the back like tiles on a roof, and a wide and tough girdle that projects everywhere beyond them. If the shells are removed from the animal they are seen to have projecting from their front edges a series of greenish plates arranged like a palisade and bearing a resemblance to a set of teeth.

Chitons are abundant on the rocks everywhere between tide marks, lurking usually in depressions where they are sheltered from the sun's rays, and the attachment of the large foot is so secure that a considerable leverage is necessary to remove them. If turned over by means of a strong knife the foot is seen as an oval, cream-coloured disk surrounded by the expansive girdle, and immediately in front of it lies the sucker-like mouth. Although Chitons are always stationary when exposed by the tide, they are capable of gliding over the surface of the rock when submerged.

SEA-HARES

We have had occasion to describe some very extraordinary devices adopted by various animals of the reef for their protection, but none is more strange or more effective than the "smoke-screen" emitted by the sea-hares. If molested they pour out from the posterior region of their bodies a great stream of violet liquid which, rapidly diffusing in the water, effectively screens them from view. The colour of this liquid, which is secreted by a special gland, resembles a solution of permanganate of potassium (Condy's crystals); as it diffuses to a low concentration it shades off to a most delicate pink.

Sea-hares are very abundant throughout the Great Barrier Reef, the commonest species, pale yellowish-brown in colour marked and spotted with dark brown, growing to a length of about fifteen inches. It is a soft and flabby creature with a small shell embedded in its flesh. The head is provided with two pairs of tentacles, one pair of which is usually very prominent and serves to heighten the resemblance of the animal to a crouching hare.

The animal crawls snail-like over the surface of the sand, or partially embedded, by means of its broad, flat foot from the edge of which folds arch upwards on each side to meet loosely overhead; when crawling over the bottom these folds are usually held widespread and disclose the mantle, which lies immediately above the degenerate shell.

The mouth is situated on the under side of the head and the animal browses on seaweeds in the vicinity of which it is usually found, though some kinds feed also on animal food and may even consume their own eggs. The eggs are laid in tangled strings which may attain a length of about twenty-four yards.

To white people the soft, flabby flesh does not attract as a possible source of food, but in some of the Pacific Islands the natives eat the animals raw and regard them, and the eggs too, as a great delicacy.

From remote times sea-hares have had an evil history, probably because of their violet secretion which was credited with having burning properties if allowed to come in contact with human flesh. Indeed, Dioscorides tells us that they are a splendid remedy for superfluous hair!

SEA-SLUGS

Even more degenerate as far as the development of shells is concerned are the sea-slugs known as Nudibranchs (naked gills) for, although shells are present in the larval stages, the adults are entirely devoid of them. The name "sea-slug" is rather an unfortunate one for it conveys an impression of a drab, slimy, and uninteresting animal, whereas the sea-slugs of the Barrier Reef are amongst the most beautiful animals to be found there. They are elongated or flat and broadly oval and may be found from about an inch to nine or ten inches in length. One of the largest, commonest, and most striking is illustrated in Plate 39; this photograph was taken while the animal was alive and it shows it in all its original beauty. Unlike most sea-slugs it is capable of swimming, and as it swims with a flowing, undulating motion it conveys the impression of a ballet dancer robed in a richly coloured cloak, the edges of the mantle folding and expanding as it glides through the water.

Toward the front of the median orange band is a pair of tentacles upon which the animal mainly relies for sensing the conditions about it; behind them and lying just beneath the surface of the skin is a pair of eyes which are capable of little more than distinguishing light from darkness. At the other extremity of the orange band is a circle of plume-like gills which can be expanded or withdrawn at will. On the under surface is an expansive flat foot by means of which the animal is able to crawl about.

Sea-slugs are extremely variable in shape, form, and colour. One more elongated species which is occasionally found hiding under stones in the daytime is a brilliant yellow crossed by a median black band and with four black spots on the posterior half of the body; others are mottled and spotted in various shades of brown and yellow.

When removed from their natural environment these sea-slugs are very conspicuous, but when moving about the reef many of them are concealed by their irregular patterns and colours, which effectively blend with their surroundings. The specimen illustrated in Plate 39, however, must be conspicuous anywhere, and it is possible that its colours serve as a warning to fish and other animals that might normally include sea-slugs in their diet, for it is not unlikely that its flesh is distasteful and irritating.

The upper surface of many sea-slugs is covered to a greater or less extent with filaments into which branches of the liver extend; the food, such as seaweed, which the slug consumes, passes into these filaments during the course of digestion and, showing through the surface, assists the animal to assume the colour of the weed amongst which it is browsing. Others feed on sea anemones (they are amongst the few animals that will brave their stinging batteries) and the poison darts pass into the projecting lobes of the body where they are stored for liberation when touched by an aggressor. A striking example of stealing the opponent's thunder!

It is not uncommon for a sea-slug to crawl over seaweed to the surface of the water where it rests upside-down, its broad foot secreting a copious supply of mucus which enables it to adhere to the surface film. The eggs of sea-slugs are deposited in a mucous envelope in the form of a spiral coil or ribbon.

If you wander round the foreshore at low tide you cannot fail to be impressed by the great quantities of shellfish such as limpets and sea-snails which cling in clusters to the rocks. Many of these are submerged during every period of high tide, but some live well above mean high-water level and are covered only during the highest spring tides. The capacity of these shellfish to resist drying in the hot sun for such long periods is remarkable; they are following in the paths of land-snails and are gradually leaving the water (as the land snails did) for an existence confined entirely to the land.

THE OCTOPUS

We now come to a type of shellfish that in many ways is the most remarkable and the most highly organized of all those embraced in this great group of molluscs—the squid, the octopus, and their allies. A superficial examination of one of these repulsive creatures fails to show a single point of resemblance to other shellfish, and the average visitor to the reef probably never associates the two. It is indeed difficult to recognize a relationship between a squid or an octopus and, say, a clam or a cowrie, yet there are features of their soft parts that are constructed on the same general plan, and although the squid is not enclosed in a shelly armour it has a degenerate shell internally, while in the octopus it is reduced to a mere vestige.

The flabby body of the octopus is shaped like a bag; from the head eight long arms, connected at their bases by a web, radiate outwards and taper till their tips are as fine as whip-lashes; their inner surfaces are studded with a double row of disks or suckers that decrease in size with the diameter of the arm. The mouth is situated on the lower surface of the head between the bases of the arms; it is provided with a large dark brown or black horny beak shaped like that of a parrot.

The two large bulgy eyes, situated on each side of its head, are constructed on the same general plan as the human eye; each is provided with a cornea, iris, lens, focusing muscles and retina, and is a very efficient organ.

The octopus usually lies under ledges or in crevices amongst the coral; it may even build a nest for itself by piling broken pieces of coral around it, and on the fore-shores of the mainland it sometimes builds such a retreat out of oysters. Crawling over the surface of a bed where the oysters are laid to mature it gathers up a quantity by affixing its suckers to them and piles them in a circular heap, hollow in the middle, where it hides. Owing to the accumulation of silt the lower oysters usually die and the octopus may therefore be at times a pest to the oyster farmer.

Securely hidden from view amongst the coral, the octopus waits and watches for its prey; should a crab or a fish pass by it shoots out a long arm, grasps it by means of its suckers and drags it to its den. Twining its arms about it, the octopus bites it with its beak, at the same time injecting digestive juices that quickly paralyse it; these it continues to pump into its victim for some time afterwards and they dissolve and partly digest the flesh which is then sucked up.

The strength of the arms of an octopus is very great, and the adhesive power of the suckers is increased by the expansion of their cavity to form a partial vacuum.

Although its normal mode of progression is by gliding its arms over the bottom, the octopus can swim rapidly backwards either by opening wide the umbrella-like web connecting the arms and then closing it forcibly, or by expelling a series of rapid jets of water from a tube-like siphon situated just below the region of the head. If molested it squirts from a special sac, known as an ink-bag, a stream of liquid sepia which quickly diffuses in the water and forms an effective screen under cover of which the octopus is usually able to effect its escape. There is also a species of octopus on the Barrier Reef that can burrow in the sand with great rapidity.

Tales of encounters with giant and fearsome octopuses are a myth. The story of the giant octopus thrusting its long arms over the side of a boat and dragging terrified sailors to their doom is perhaps good fiction, but it has no basis in fact.

THE SQUID

There are some species of squid, however, that may grow to an enormous size, and there are records of giant squid that have reached a length of upwards of fifty feet. These, however, usually inhabit deep water, and the squid that are found in the shallow water of the reef rarely exceed a few feet in length. The true squid has an internal shell that is elongated, narrow, and of horny consistency; it has received the name of "sea-pen," and on account of the sepia ink the animal produces it has been designated "the clerk of the sea." The cuttle-fish has a more massive bony shell in the form of a long oval; it is commonly found washed up by the tide and quantities are gathered for mixing with poultry food after being ground. The term "squid," however, is frequently applied to this animal also, and on account of their general resemblance no further attempt will be made to differentiate between the two here.

There are important differences between the squid and the octopus, however. The body of the squid is more or less cylindrical and it is provided on each side with a fin-like appendage by means of which it swims slowly either forwards or backwards, the body being held horizontally. If, however, it is pursued it swims backwards like the octopus with great speed by forcible ejections of water through the

PLATE 27.

RED HERMIT CRAB IN A FALSE HELMET SHELL
(Three-quarters natural size.)

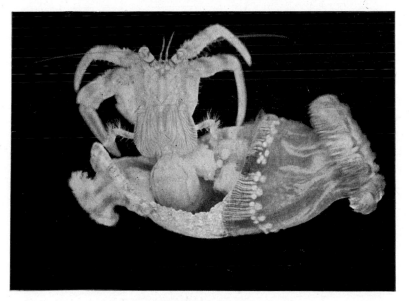

HERMIT CRAB

This crab is afforded added protection by two stinging anemones attached
to its borrowed shell. (Three-fifths natural size.)

siphon. Another important difference lies in the possession by the squid of eight normal arms and two others that may be very elongated; these are provided with suckers near the tip only, and as the animal swims they are generally kept curled up out of the way, but on the approach of prey they are suddenly shot out to seize it.

Now, much has been said and written about the power of the chameleon to change its colour, but it is a mere novice in the art compared with the squid and its allies. The range of colour they are capable of assuming and the rapidity with which it can be altered are remarkable and probably unsurpassed by any other member of the animal kingdom. This was forcibly impressed on me one day when I was photographing coral life in colour at Heron Island in the Capricorn Group. I was developing some plates in the dark-room that had been prepared for my use in the disused turtle factory when a tourist returning from the reef called to me that he had brought in a squid. On inquiry whether it showed much colour he informed me that it was very beautiful, so I directed him to place it in a large tub containing sea-water and sand. This he accordingly did and then made back to the reef. On completion of my developing I went out to inspect it and found it—the colour of sand! For a moment I thought my friend was having a joke at my expense, but then the cause suddenly dawned on me. Procuring a piece of black card I placed it beneath the animal, and in a very short time it had assumed the colours shown in Plate 35, fig. 2.

The flesh of the squid provides excellent bait. As soon as I had photographed the specimen illustrated, which had an overall measurement of twenty inches, it was taken for use as bait by several tourists who were about to do some angling just beyond the reef crest, and later in the day they returned with forty-three fish averaging about three pounds each—and part of the unused squid.

The colour-changes of the squid and its relatives may be completely under the control of the animal, when they are altered to blend with their environment, but they are also apparently subject to emotional changes; if harassed, a wide range of colours will sweep over its surface with intervening periods of complete absence of colour. This alteration is brought about by the action of pigment cells in the skin; these contain a range of colours and the contraction of certain of the cells gives full play to others which contain the colour it is desired to assume.

When pursued by a foe such as a fish the squid adopts several artful ruses. First, in an effort to confuse its adversary it will suddenly change its course and its colour several times, but if this is of no avail in throwing off its pursuer it will emit a great cloud of sepia and double off at right angles when its adversary is usually completely confused, and the squid streaks away in the distance.

A further adaptation has been evolved by some species of squid that live in the abysses of the ocean where, owing to the inky blackness that prevails there, the secretion of sepia would be of no value at all; there they may squirt out a luminous cloud that serves the same purpose.

The water-colour pigment known as sepia is obtained from certain species of squid, the dried contents of the ink-bags being dissolved in dilute ammonia and precipitated with hydrochloric acid.

Very small squid are occasionally found in great abundance in Barrier Reef waters where they are preyed upon by many species of fish and birds. The very large species form one of the principal foods of the sperm whale, and the valuable product of this whale known as ambergris is frequently found to contain numbers of their beaks embedded in its substance.

Although both the octopus and the squid are frequently seen in Australian fish markets they are bought only for use as bait; in Mediterranean countries, however, they are regularly used as food, the smaller kinds bringing a good price.

THE NAUTILUS AND THE ARGONAUT

An interesting relative of the octopus and squid is the pearly nautilus which has an external shell composed of many chambers, in the last of which it lives; each of these chambers is connected with the one preceding it, thereby allowing the specific gravity to be raised or lowered at will. The numerous tentacles of the pearly nautilus are not provided with suckers.

Another relative, known as the paper argonaut, is renowned for the beautifully sculptured and delicate white shell in which the female rests. This shell is open and cradle-like, slightly coiled towards the back, and is not attached to the animal at all; it is held clasped to her body by two specially modified arms which are flattened and expanded at their extremities and are responsible for its construction. In this cradle the eggs are laid and hatched while carried about the ocean. The diminutive male, having no responsibility in the caring for the eggs, is incapable of building a cradle and roams about naked throughout its life.

The shell of the paper argonaut is always regarded by tourists on the reef as a prize when found washed up on the beaches.

CHAPTER
ELEVEN   *Interlude*

W HEN staying as a guest of the British Barrier Reef
    Expedition at Low Island in 1928 I became greatly
interested in a little aboriginal boy, Cecil Andrew Dabah,
aged five, and his elder sister, Edith, whose age was seven.
They were the children of one, Andy, who was doing the
duties of general rouseabout, and Mrs Andy, who did the
cooking (and did it very well) for the members of the
Expedition. Edith waited on the table and an efficient little
waitress she was. Barefooted, she would move along behind us; a thin, dark arm would steal out beside us, and
a plate or a cup would disappear as if wafted into thin
air, shortly to be replaced by another at the end of the
same thin, dark arm. Although the kitchen was immediately
adjoining, Edith apparently repeated our orders to her
mother in whispers or perhaps conveyed our desires by signs,
for never did we hear the sound of voices from within.

But it was Andrew who intrigued me more. When playing with his sister he was as happy as a sand-boy; his dusky
little face was perpetually wrapt in smiles (Plate 20, fig. 1),
often to burst forth into ecstatic laughter, displaying a
double row of teeth that glistened like bleached coral; his
voice, gutteral, musical, could be heard as he talked with
his sister in the distance—in the distance always, for at my
approach he would cease his chatter instantly; he was shy,
sensitive. I could not help likening him to a hermit crab

PLATE 28.

A LARGE HERMIT CRAB
This crab had taken up its quarters in a bailer-shell. One-half natural size.

which, unmolested and free from danger, would go about
its daily tasks boldly, unafraid, but at our approach would
withdraw into its shell, its eyes on long stalks always alert,
but little else to be seen. Both were primitive creatures of
nature.

I wanted Andrew to talk to me; his distant voice was
music in my ears. I wanted to judge the standard of his
intelligence; to discover his outlook on life; to find out
what he thought of us white people surrounded with all
the curious paraphernalia connected with scientific marine
investigation. And so at every available opportunity I spoke
to him, encouraged him, cajoled him. But not a word
would he utter. To my questions, a smile and a nod or a
shake of the head, but never a single yes or no.

Day after day I tried to break down the barrier that
he had erected about him. Day after day the same charming
smile, the same nod or shake of the head. Baffled continually, I felt that this lad's shyness was accompanied by a certain stubbornness which only served to increase my determination to break through his stony silence.

One day he was laid up; an infected foot had to be
lanced. Although obviously suffering considerable pain he
gave no indication that he felt it. He was a little stoic, and
my interest, till now springing from the head rather than
the heart, grew into a deep affection. I sat on his bed and
told him fairy stories; he had a toy drum decorated with
the flags of many nations; I told him about the peoples of
those countries. I told him about my own two children,
about my daughter Norma and my little son Clive. Pointing to the south I told him I came from a great big town
called Sydney, about the shops and the multitude of people
who thronged the streets (there was no harbour bridge to
talk about then). His eyes would glow as every now and

κ

again some incident in my story would quicken his imagination; but I wanted to know how much of my stories his primitive intelligence was absorbing, and occasionally I would ask him a question; I would try to catch him unawares. If he would only say "yes" I should feel I had accomplished something. But his vigilance never relaxed; with a pronounced nod and beaming countenance he would signify a reply in the affirmative.

The following day I again approached his bed and with an air now of great familiarity I breezily greeted him with, "Well, old boy, how is the foot this morning?" A broad grin was his only reply. I was getting desperate; I must be on the wrong line of approach; there must be some key that would unlock this lad's silence. But for the life of me I could not find it.

I endeavoured to discover how much of my previous day's chat he had absorbed, or even if he remembered any of it, and so I chided him by telling him he didn't know where I lived. A shake of the head seemed to indicate that he remembered nothing. Suddenly I took from my pocket a threepence, and holding it before him I said, "Andrew, if you can tell me where I live I will give you this." "Sydney," he instantly replied.

My little friend, whose near ancestors were people of the stone age, was mercenary! The lure of a piece of silver had accomplished what my friendship, sympathy, and solicitude had hopelessly failed to do.

At last the barrier was down; from that moment Andrew chatted freely, and he answered all my questions without hesitation. He gave me full value for my money. At last I was to gain an insight into his intelligence, and I marvelled at the way he had absorbed every word I had told him. His memory was remarkable.

From that day Andrew followed me about; if I was interested in hermit crabs he came to me with handfuls of them; if now my attention was directed to shells he always searched for the attractive ones.

Eventually the day came when I had to leave the island. Andrew and Edith expressed their pleasure at my stay, their sorrow at my departure. I was sorry indeed to leave them.

From Low Island a launch took me to Port Douglas, once a prosperous mining centre, now drowsily living on memories of the past. After a few hours here I left on the launch which trades regularly between Port Douglas and Cairns. Leaving at 5 p.m., the forty-mile journey was expected to occupy five hours, but we had not proceeded far before a stiff breeze from the south sprang up and rain came down in torrents. There was no shelter on the launch and in a very short time all the passengers (there were five of us) were wet to the skin. To some who seemed to find great comfort in leaning over the side of the launch the rain was of little consequence.

To me the marvel of this trip was the skill of the navigator. Through the black night, through rain so thick that visibility was reduced to a few yards, the skipper took his boat along a maze of channels bordered with walls of coral that a hundred times would have spelled disaster to one not thoroughly acquainted with every foot of the journey. He had sailed these waters since childhood.

It was after midnight when, with a sigh of relief, we reached the shelter of Cairns harbour, and a welcome supper was waiting for us at our hotel. Our hospitable host had waited up to attend to our personal comfort. The following day I ordered a large tin of sweets to be forwarded to my two young friends on Low Island.

Proceeding to Brisbane to plan an investigation of the

oyster resources of Queensland which I had been requested to undertake for the Queensland Government, I spent the next month on the waters of Moreton Bay, Port Curtis, and Sandy Straits. On the completion of this task I returned to the hotel at Brisbane which I had made my headquarters during the periods that intervened between my work in the field, and I was surprised to find a letter on the rack addressed to me in a childish handwriting. It was from Edith. How she found out where I was staying remains with me to this day a mystery. This letter is reproduced on page 133; I have kept it as a cherished memento. I sent Edith a doll and Andrew a train, and received the delightful acknowledgment reproduced on page 134. Here we have the scholastic efforts of a girl of seven, a juvenile member of a race that has been described as the most primitive of all native races; whose culture was little higher than that of the people of the stone age; here was a girl whose education at a mission station lacked the intensity of that of our ordinary schools, whose environment from early childhood had lacked the parental example of correct grammatical English. And this letter, I venture to say, would compare favourably with that of most white children of the same age. One notes the conventional "just a few lines" and "I think I will close," common amongst many letter-writers of a generation ago, even to-day.

Before we leave our little friends we cannot help wondering what their lives would have been if they had been left in the wilds uninfluenced by contact with whites and their modern artificial standards of living. No tins of sweets; no dolls; no trains that "wistle"; no school; no clothes even. Would they have been happier? It is hard to say. These children receive wonderful enjoyment from simple toys, but the restraint of a mission station and the regular

PLATE 29.

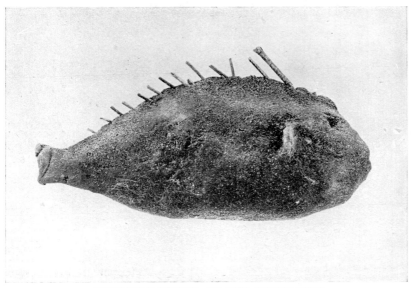

BEES-WAX MODEL OF THE STONE-FISH
Used by the aborigines of the Cooktown district during their initiation
ceremonies.

Photo: H. Barnes.

THE MUD-SKIPPER
This fish, seen here basking in the sun and breathing through its tail, will
drown if kept under water.

Photo: T. C. Roughley.

PLATE 30.

HAULING A DEVIL RAY ON BOARD

Fortunately, this huge fish, which may grow to about a ton in weight, is quite harmless.

Photo: Milton Kent.

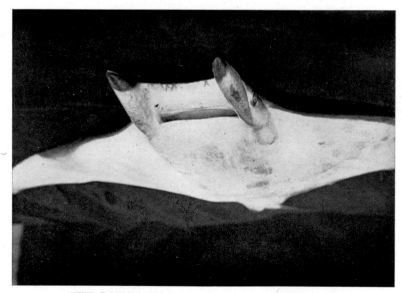

THE LOWER SURFACE OF THE HORNED RAY

The "horns" probably assist the fish to gather its food.

Photo: T. C. Roughley.

Low Iles
Port Douglas
Aug 29. 928

Our Dear Friend.

Just a few lines. to let
you know. that we got the tin of sweets
safe. an we thankes you very very much
for your kindes. to my little Brother an
to me. you doant know. how pleased. my
Brother. an I was. when we saw. the
graite big tin of sweets. how did you
like been up heare. me an my little
Brother often talk about you. how are
your. little girl. an boy. my Brother an
I hope to see you agin. some day. I whant
a Photo of your self. my Brother. sends his
best Love to you an kiss. from us boathe.. all so
Farther an Mother sends theire best wishes.
to you. has your little girl got any old
dolls. I would like one. old one from her..
my Brother say he whant a little train. from
your little boy. well dear Friend I will
close. I remane your little Friend.

Miss Edith Dabah

best Love from me an Andrew
+ + + + + + +

sour I ls Port Douglas

Our Dearest Friend.

Just a few lines. to thank you very.
very. much. for the lovely. Present. that you sent to
me an. my little Brother . it was a graite big suprise
to us . how. good an kind of you. to send this Lovely big
doll .for me . an it calls out mamma, an my Brothers
train . wisties when it runs. I will take a grate care
of my Lovely big doll. Beacuse I never had a
big doll given to me before. this is the first doll
I had . an my little Brother never had a lovely
train like this one . an my Mother an Farther was
pleased. with our lovely Present. an Mother is
going to get my big sister to do some fancy
work. for Normas Mother . we are going to send some
thing .for you. an Norma. an b live. well. our dear
big sweetheart. I think I will. Close. it is very hot
now. yes I for got to tell you my dolly Name is
Norma. an tell your little Norma. we have one
Norma heare to . Mother an Farther sends their. very
best wishes. an kind regards. to you an all of your Family.
best love frome my Brother an myself. an kiss.
Edith x x + + + + + + little Andrew x x + +
we are going home to Jarrabah. this mounth.
if you write. send our letters to Jarrabah. Mission
                                    Cairns.

attendance at school must prove very irksome; there is a restlessness in their lives that a modern education cannot eradicate.

"HERRIN'S"

On one occasion during my stay at Heron Island I was photographing some Pandanus-trees at the southern extremity of the island when my attention was attracted by several dark masses in the water a few yards from the beach. They puzzled me. Obviously they were not patches of coral which everywhere showed as bluish-grey areas beneath the surface of the water. Yet they could scarcely be fish for they were as stationary as solid rock. On completion of the task that engaged my immediate attention I went to the water's edge, and picking up a small stone I threw it into the nearest of them. It quickly parted in the middle and then slowly closed again to a uniform density. It was composed of small fishes so densely packed that their bodies must surely have been touching.*

I was very anxious to capture some in order to determine what they were, and so hurried back to the camp to obtain a suitable net. Unfortunately none was at hand, so in the absence of the cook from the kitchen I borrowed his colander. Fishes packed as these were should surely be captured in a colander. But though I stalked them with all the care possible they always moved *en masse* just beyond my reach; I persevered for about half an hour but they continued to elude and at last, my patience exhausted, I gave up the chase.

Returning to the camp I found the cook installed in his kitchen and asked him if he had seen these dense shoals of fishes; if he had ever captured any of them; did he know what they were. "Oh," replied the cook, "they're herrin's;

---

* Two of these shoals can be seen just beyond the rocks in Plate 41.

the island's named after them." After reconsidering the matter carefully, he added, "I am not quite sure whether the island is called after them or the birds."

Later I took some of the visitors to see them, and a business genius in the party decided to establish a sardine factory on the spot. Sardines ready packed appealed to him as a wonderful proposition.

Subsequent captures showed the fishes to be hardyheads. They are usually present in shoals of varying magnitude and at times may almost completely surround the island. They are common round many of the islands in the Capricorn and other groups farther north.

A CLOSE CALL

On another occasion during my stay at Heron Island I had rather an eventful day, which nearly ended in tragedy. A boat party had decided to spend the day fishing on a ground some miles away and it was arranged that I should be dropped on Wistari Reef* to do some collecting and obtain some photographs of the beautiful mauve corals that abound there. Wistari Reef is a large reef that submerges to a depth of several feet at high tide; at low tide the reef edge is bared and encloses an expansive body of water and coral. When we arrived there the tide was fairly low and I was rowed ashore in a dinghy. I made for a large nigger-head close by and decided to establish this as my base. To my astonishment the launch made back towards Heron Island. This rather mystified me, but it returned about an hour later, and hailing me the skipper shouted that they had returned for the lunches, which had been forgotten. He was sorry that he couldn't bring my lunch ashore, for the state of the tide and the choppy sea made the approach to the reef dangerous. I told

---

* Known locally as Wistaria Reef.

him not to worry for I was perfectly comfortable, but later in the day I began to feel a little sorry for myself, for one gets very hungry—and thirsty—in the open air all day.

However, soon after the time when I considered my fishing friends would be consuming copious bottles of lunch, I was lying on the edge of a coral pool absorbingly interested in the multi-hued fish that swam leisurely about below me, when my subconscious mind registered a great booming noise in the distance. At last I stood up and looked in the direction whence the sounds came and the sight that met my gaze fairly filled me with amazement. First I saw far in the distance what appeared to be a huge bird leap with outstretched wings high in the air. It was a giant devil ray leaping in mad fury to escape the attack of some enemy beneath. This was quickly followed by whale after whale which, leaping and turning, their white bellies flashing in the sunlight, threw up great clouds of spray as they struck the water with a report like a cannon shot. Armed with a stop-watch I was able to check the time taken for the sound to reach me, and it showed that this fierce onslaught was just three miles away. The distance was far too great for me to determine the cause, but, although I believe that great sharks will attack whales in these waters I cannot conceive that such turmoil could have been caused by other than killer whales, which frequently harass their larger relatives as they return to Antarctic waters with their calves.

I was having an eventful day, but an unwelcome surprise was in store for me.

As the day wore on the tide began to flow over the reef edge and made further observations impossible. Hastening to my nigger-head base I arrived just in time to save one of my cameras, resting on a low-lying ledge, from being washed away. Quickly I transferred all my gear to its summit and sat beside it. It was about four o'clock and the tide was now coming in with a rush. But there was much to interest me. Fish of various kinds followed the tide across the reef edge. From my elevated vantage-point I was able to watch huge sting-rays and eels pass within a few feet of me. I began to wonder what had happened to the launch; it should have come into sight long ago. Supposing they couldn't start that engine. . . .

The sun sank below the horizon a ball of fire, casting a ruddy glow over a cloudless sky; as it disappeared the sea beneath lost its sheen of burnished gold and turned a deep, purplish blue. It was all very beautiful, but my nigger-head, weathered into crags, was far from comfortable and I began to feel very cramped. It was now half under water; at full tide it would be submerged to a depth of several feet, and the tide was rising rapidly, relentlessly. Every now and again a wave, bigger than its fellows, would dash against the rock and shake it unsteadily, throwing a shower of spray over me and my cameras. About twenty yards away several large triangular fins were slowly cleaving the water in a semicircle; I began to imagine that the sharks just beneath the surface were grinning at me. They seemed to know. As I watched them, fascinated, I thought that after all their race owed me nothing, for had I not for many years advocated their wholesale destruction for the commercial products they yielded? For years I had been striving to develop an industry that would lead to their slaughter without any show of mercy.

A large devil ray, the tips of its expansive fins breaking the water together as they rhythmically reached the top of their sweep, passed by leisurely. Thank heavens, devil rays were harmless.

From the ray my eyes searched the sea, now a deep

greyish-blue in the dusk; the water was very close to the surface of the rock; I stood up the better to see, the better to be seen. I was a mere speck in the ocean vastness; not another object broke the surface—except those fins. They began to annoy me.

Suddenly from out the dusk cheers rent the air, and, looking in the direction whence they came, I saw the hazy outline of the launch. Quickly a dinghy pulled in alongside me and in a few minutes I was safely on board, to find everybody very relieved; all had had an anxious time and I am afraid some despaired of locating me in the gathering darkness. Explanations soon followed and once more we headed for the island—and comfort.

The delay of the launch was caused by the fact that some of the anglers, feeling a little unstable in the choppy sea, decided to go ashore on the far extremity of the reef, several miles away. The dinghy remained with them, and, forgetting that I was to be picked up they did not return to the launch till very late. It was an unenviable experience, but I learnt a lesson never to land on a reef which is covered at high tide without a dinghy always handy.

AN EFFICIENT COLLECTOR

One of the most difficult of the reef animals to capture is the mantis prawn. Although everywhere very prevalent it is extremely alert, and on your approach will quickly dash for the cover of adjacent coral or disappear down a burrow it has constructed in the sand. I badly wanted some specimens to photograph, for some are very beautiful and their structure is rather interesting. But try as I would I was never even near success. Perhaps I was a little afraid of them, for, although I continually wore thick leather gloves when collecting on the reef, they have powerful nippers which terminate in points as sharp as needles, and they use them fiercely.

Discussing my difficulty one night with a party of visitors on the island, one of them, a former boxing champion of Victoria, guaranteed to catch a specimen for me. I was very sceptical and warned him about its formidable nippers. Next day he returned from the reef with two beautiful specimens; he had several nasty gashes in his hands but that didn't trouble him. He had fulfilled his promise; what else mattered?

He then told me that he had seen several sea-snakes in pools on the reef and inquired whether I wanted any. Of course I did; but I warned him to exercise great caution for they are all very venomous. Next day he returned with two beautiful reef eels. He thought they were sea-snakes and after a strenuous chase he grabbed them behind the head. My boxing friend was a good collector.

BRISTLES

After a few days' exploration of the reef at Heron Island the tip of the index finger of my right hand became numbed following an aggravating irritation. This puzzled me greatly for I had not handled any specimens except with my hands protected by thick leather gloves. Then one day I was on the reef with Captain Poulson, who leases the island, and on turning over a stone I came across a bristle worm about a foot long (Plate 20, fig. 2). I had handled hundreds of similar worms, or what appeared on cursory examination to be similar worms, on the coast of New South Wales where they are used extensively as bait, and grasping this one lightly between my gloved fingers I threw it across to Captain Poulson, telling him to keep it for bait. "You are not asking me to pick that up, are you?" he replied. "Why not,"

PLATE 31.

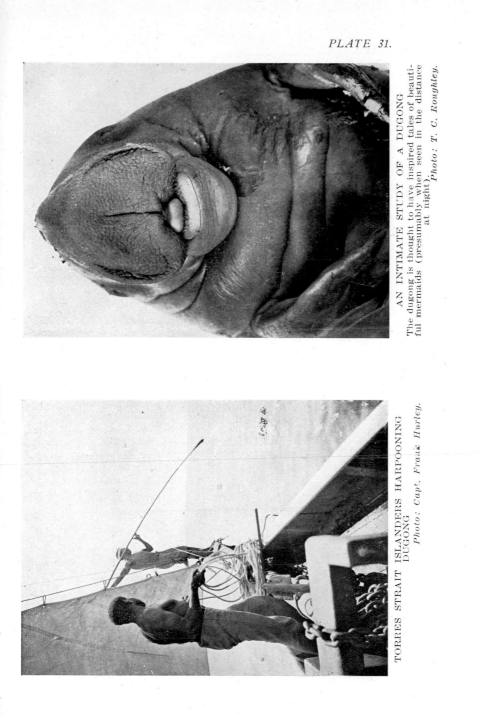

AN INTIMATE STUDY OF A DUGONG

The dugong is thought to have inspired tales of beautiful mermaids (presumably when seen in the distance at night).

Photo: T. C. Roughley.

TORRES STRAIT ISLANDERS HARPOONING DUGONG

Photo: Capt. Frank Hurley.

PLATE 32.

NEST OF THE GREEN TREE-ANT
The leaves are sewn together by means of a silky secretion exuded by the larval ants.

A GREEN TREE-ANTS' "COW-SHED"
The ants have imprisoned a number of mealy bugs (coccids) in order to prevent them from straying.

Photos: T. C. Roughley.

I said, "it is wonderful bait." "I'm not touching that," he retorted, "it is a mass of prickles."

Taking off my glove I found hundreds of fine white spines embedded in the tip of my index finger; the leather glove had offered no resistance to them at all. If there is anything in the world sharper than the bristles of this worm I should like to see it, but please hand it to me on a plate. The tip of my finger remained partially numbed for six weeks afterwards.

THE aborigines of the Cooktown district in northern Queensland periodically perform elaborate ceremonies when initiating members of the tribe into the privileges of full citizenship. These ceremonies extend over several weeks and take place in a circular clearing prepared by removing all bushes and leaves, and levelling the ground.

The elders of the tribe dance round and round the edge of the clearing while a chosen three carry out the symbolic ceremonies near its centre. Varied and weird are these performances which are for the most part based on the habits of the animals the blacks are familiar with, such as snakes, birds, crabs, mosquitoes and—body lice.

In the dance of the body louse the two outside performers pull the head of the middle one about unmercifully as they seek the elusive vermin, and, uttering ejaculations of satisfaction as they find them, they promptly eat them— or rather pretend to, for after all the whole ceremony is a piece of realistic acting. Having rid the victim's head of the creatures they continue the search by exploring other likely portions of his body.

THE POISONOUS STONE-FISH

Such a ceremony is typical of the many performed daily for the edification of the uninitiated. But the one which at the moment interests us most is that devoted to another vile creature, the stone-fish (Plate 21, fig. 1), or "dornorn," as these blacks call it, the spines on the back of which are extremely venomous. While the backs of the novices are turned a bees-wax model of the fish with bones or sticks stuck into it in a row along the back (Plate 29, fig. 1) is concealed on the ground near the centre of the sacred area. At a given signal the novitiates are allowed to gaze on the scene. Round the circle the elders continue their dance with a monotonous guttural chant and much gesticulating, while the three central performers are energetically thrusting their spears downwards, obviously in an endeavour to transfix something. At last one of them treads on the stone-fish; he falls to the ground in a paroxysm of pain and shrieks and writhes in agony. The model is then "discovered" and exhibited to the novices.

Clearly, the stone-fish is held in great respect by these keen-sighted aborigines, and well it might be for it is as venomous as a snake. It occurs throughout the whole of the Great Barrier Reef, but is more often found in the northern than in the southern area; fortunately it appears to be nowhere very prevalent although it is possibly more common than it seems, for it is extraordinarily well camouflaged and frequently half buries itself amongst sand and coral debris.

The stone-fish has no redeeming feature. If it is the world's most poisonous fish it is probably also the world's most ugly fish; indeed, it is about as loathsome as any creature on land or in the sea. Its body, soft and slimy, is just a mass of horrible warty excrescences; its great upwardly-directed mouth is a sickly green inside; its movements are sluggish and altogether lacking the grace of other fish. Its repulsiveness is complete.

But if nature has treated it abominably in the way of looks, it would seem that its whole disposition has soured in consequence, and one could almost imagine that it has made an effort to retaliate by subjecting to a painful death every living thing that touches it. Extending along the back from behind the head almost as far as the tail are thirteen spines (thirteen? yes, one would almost think it knew), each as sharp as a needle, each provided with two venom glands, each effectively concealed by innocent wart-like coverings forming a sheath that readily slips away from the point. Normally, these spines lie flat along the back, but on the moment they are touched they stand up, erect and rigid, and as they penetrate the flesh the venom is carried along grooves in their sides to enter deep into the punctured wound.

The venom is probably a nerve poison; there is no known antidote, and if injected into human beings it causes a prolonged agony that is wellnigh unbearable. A number of fatalities have occurred as a result of handling or treading on stone-fish, while in other cases the patients have been laid up for months with frequently recurring attacks of excruciating pain. Under treatment the pain is usually alleviated to some extent by copious injections of opium. But that is not all. As a second line of defence many of the warty tubercles when touched squirt out a milky fluid which is also believed to be poisonous.

Effectively armoured as it is, the stone-fish makes no attempt to dash for cover at our approach. Apparently confident of the effectiveness of its camouflage as it lies amongst the coral, not only its broken contour but its colour harmonizing with its surroundings, it simply waits and watches, secure in the knowledge that certain death will overtake all the denizens of the reef that dare to molest it. And as it waits, motionless, just an eroded piece of coral, it is freely approached by other fishes and crabs unsuspicious of the lurking death that awaits their coming, then one swift gulp and down the great cavity they go—never to return.

So dense is its coating of slime that the fish resembles a piece of dead and decaying coral, but if the slime is removed the underlying skin may be distinctly beautiful, perhaps mottled with brown, grey, violet, and yellow.

What an extraordinary creature this is! Does it not convey the almost irresistible impression that, like a rejected suitor, it has deliberately gone to the dogs, discarding all virtues, knowing no friends? But, of course, it really cannot help itself; it has simply evolved that way and is no more responsible for its appearance and apparent misdeeds than any other product of nature's handiwork.

Did I say that it hasn't one virtue? I am wrong; strange as it may seem, beneath its hideous exterior it has a wholesome flesh which is relished by the Chinese.

Lest the reader may hesitate to walk over the reef for fear of treading on this fish I may say that with heavy soles on his shoes the possibility of an unwelcome encounter with it may be forgotten. Thousands roam about the reef every year, and it is many years since trouble from a stone-fish has been recorded.

THE BUTTERFLY COD

But let us leave this loathsome creature and pass on to a subject more pleasing. If we rest quietly beside a coral pool we may, if we are lucky, catch a glimpse of the most ornate of all coral fishes, the butterfly cod. There are many fishes more brilliantly coloured than this, but for comeliness and beauty and grace none can surpass it. Its zebra-like body is covered with vertical scarlet stripes of irregular width on a creamy ground; its great expansive dorsal and pectoral fins open like fans richly decorated with similar stripes, the individual rays with trailing feather-like edges;

L

the tail and anal fin are beautifully spotted, while the huge ventral fins are a rich greenish-purple conspicuously splashed with white.

The butterfly cod is never in a hurry; it moves slowly about with a quiet dignity reminiscent of the peacock. What a contrast is this pride of the pool to the stone-fish! Yet both belong to the same family, which embraces many forbidding members; it is a Cinderella oblivious of the misdeeds of her ugly sisters. It grows to a length of about twelve inches.

THE MUD-SKIPPER

If the stone-fish is the most horrid fish of the reef; if the butterfly cod is the most beautiful, then the mud-skipper or walking-fish (Plate 29, fig. 2) is surely the most interesting and comical. Interesting because it lives more out of water than in it, comical—well, if you saw a fish staring at you intently with one eye elevated above its head while it moved the other in all directions in search of prey, you would surely class it as one of the most ludicrous objects you had ever seen.

The mud-skipper has a distribution over the reef confined to those islands, such as Low Island, east of Port Douglas, where mud-flats are uncovered at low tide. These flats always support a growth of mangroves, and it is on the mud and about the stilt-like roots of the mangroves that the mud-skipper loves to bask in the sun and to forage when the tide is out.

It is a small goby and may grow to a length of about ten inches; in colour it is an olive green or brown with blotches on the sides which serve well to camouflage it on the sun-spotted mud.

The mud-skipper is a piscatorial paradox—it will drown if kept under water! When the mud-flats are exposed scores of these small fish may be seen on the surface and even a foot or two above it clinging to the sloping roots of the mangroves. If undisturbed they move about slowly with a rowing motion of the pectoral (side) fins which are strong, flexible, and fleshy at their bases; thrusting them forwards they lever the body along aided by a pushing motion of the pelvic fins. But if they are frightened they skip over the surface of the mud and the water with great agility.

I have a lasting recollection of a day when from Cairns I journeyed to a mangrove-fringed mud-flat with a local resident for the purpose of securing specimens of these fish, which I had always assumed to be clumsy when out of water. My friend watched me from a small jetty as I entered the mud clad in heavy rubber boots extending well up my thighs. Down I sank below the knees in the oozy slime. Dragging each leg alternately out of the mud with the help of both hands I made after my quarry, which abounded everywhere over the flat. I have never had an experience quite so exasperating; the little brutes seemed to think it was a game they were playing; they would encourage me on by remaining perfectly motionless till I was within a foot or two of them and just as I would thrust out my hand they would skip away and flop into a shallow pool or down a crab-burrow to leave me completely nonplussed. Now, these small pools were only two or three inches deep and I expected to scoop the fish out quite easily, but they were never in the pools when I got there. Thinking they perhaps hid in the mud just beneath the surface I bailed out great handfuls of it in quick succession, but never was a fish to be found there. They are apparently as agile in the mud as they are above it. At last, after about an hour, I was perspiring, panting, and nearly exhausted, when one of them left his run a little too late, and the game was over.

Now, the hunt was exasperating enough, but it was rendered infinitely more so by the uproarious laughter of my companion; the more impatient I became the more he seemed to enjoy it until I thought at last he would become completely hysterical. At length, splashing through the boggy mud I returned to the jetty with my prize and inquired what there was about this fish-hunting excursion that made it appear so laughable. "Oh," he said, "your antics in the mud were funny enough, goodness knows, but I couldn't help picturing your efforts to escape if a crocodile had put in an appearance." Well, of course, that would have been funny! "But, good heavens, man," I said, "you didn't tell me there were crocodiles about here." "No," he replied, "I know what you scientists are; I didn't think it would be any use; if you chaps want anything I am sure a little thing like a crocodile wouldn't deter you." I wonder.

The mud-skipper not only skips over the mud, but it skims equally well over the surface of the water; if chased on the bank of a narrow stream it will skip across to the other side without once submerging. If disturbed on the root of a mangrove it may escape by jumping from root to root. It appears not to be fond of the water, preferring the sun and air. Its food consists of insects and small crustaceans such as crabs which it frequently captures by jumping at them.

Why is it that this, a true fish, can live for such long periods out of water when other fishes quickly suffocate? The explanation lies in the enlarged cavity that contains the gills; it encloses air as well as water, and the surrounding tissue is able to absorb oxygen from the air and thus carries out the function of a primitive lung.

But it also breathes in another way. The mud-skipper is frequently seen lying on the edge of a pool with its tail

PLATE 33.

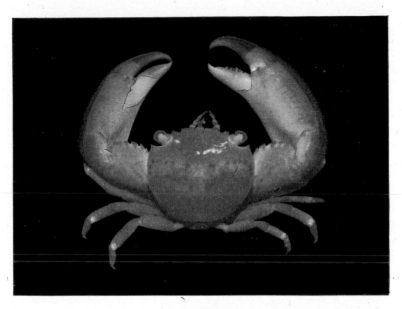

CORAL CRAB
The claws of this crab are heavier than the rest of its body.
(One and one-half times natural size.)

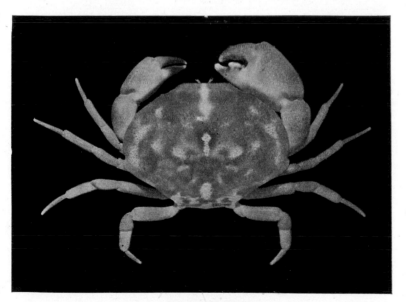

CORAL CRAB
(Two-thirds natural size.)

in the water (Plate 29, fig. 2); now, the tail is very
thin-walled and oxygen dissolved in the water can pass
through to reach the minute blood-vessels that are abundantly distributed just beneath the surface.

In other words, this extraordinary fish can breathe
through its tail!

THE SUCKER-FISH

While on the subject of extremes, we may as well consider
the laziest fish on the reef, the sucker-fish or remora, which
I suppose may be classed as the laziest fish in the world.
Although quite a strong swimmer, although well able to
forage for itself, it prefers to cling to the skin of other
animals, such as sharks and turtles, and get carried about
without any effort to itself, lunching off the scraps that its
larger host overlooks.

The sucker-fish, long and narrow, grows to a length of
three or four feet; situated on the top of its head is an
elongated oval disk (Plate 21, fig. 2) extending from the
tip of the upper jaw to behind the insertion of the pectoral
fins; in the specimen illustrated the disk measured seven
inches long, the fish itself being three feet. The disk is
an extraordinary modification of the dorsal fin; it consists
of a series of plates arranged as in a Venetian blind, all
pointing backwards with their edges covered with back-
wardly-directed teeth; they are in two parallel series separated along the middle line by a membranous partition.
Each series varies in number in different fishes from twenty-
two to twenty-five.

When a sucker-fish attaches itself to a turtle, shark, or
other large fish it depresses the base of the disk and so
creates a partial vacuum which forms an extremely powerful attachment. The arrangement of the plates is such that
the fish can free itself without effort by swimming forward,

but if an attempt is made to remove it by pulling it from behind, so secure is the adhesion that the flesh of the fish is likely to tear apart before the disk is detached. It seems probable, indeed, that when pulled backwards the fish is quite unable to let go.

The sucker-fish was well known to the ancients, and if we can believe all accounts, it has had an important influence on the destinies of nations. Was not Mark Antony delayed at the battle of Actium by the attachment of many sucker-fish to his galleys, which so impeded his progress that he was caught at a tactical disadvantage and suffered a heavy defeat? Or was it the even stronger "attachment" of Cleopatra?

In early writings the sucker-fish was known as the reversus or "upside-down" fish, the impression apparently being current at the time that it swam on its back; this, however, is incorrect for it swims quite normally.

But the chief interest in the sucker-fish lies in the fact that it has been used for countless ages by many native races as a means of catching larger fish such as sharks, and also dugongs, porpoises, and dolphins; the principal object sought, however, was the turtle.

It is worthy of note that almost identically similar methods were employed over an area extending from Madagascar in Africa to Venezuela in South America; it was used in the same way in the West Indies, China, Singapore, the Caribbean Sea, Torres Strait, and along the whole length of the Great Barrier Reef. One can only assume that it is a very ancient method of fishing and has been spread by the various races as they migrated further afield. In all cases the technique was similar, except that some native fishermen secured the line by means of a ring above the forked tail while others were content to tie it there without the use of a ring.

The aborigines of the Barrier Reef angled for the sucker-fish with lines woven from bark fibres and a hook made from bone or pearl-shell. Having captured it they fastened a line securely above the tail and tethered it in shallow water till such time as it was desired to hunt the turtles, so beloved by them as food. At the appropriate time a couple of blacks armed with three or four harpoons would proceed to sea in a frail bark canoe with scarcely more than an inch of free-board. We shall let our friend Banfield describe for us the subsequent operations:

"In sight of the game the sucker which has been adhering to the bottom of the canoe is tugged off and thrown in its direction. As a preliminary the disk and shoulders of the sucker are vigorously scrubbed with dry sand or the palm of the hand, to remove the slime and to excite the ruling passion of the fish. It makes a dash for a more congenial companionship than an insipid canoe. The line by which it is secured is made from the bark of the 'Boo-bah' (*Ficus fasciculata*) and is of two strands, so light as not to seriously encumber the sucker, and yet strong enough to withstand a considerable strain. Two small loops are made in the line about an interval of two fathoms from the sucker, to act as indicators.

"As soon as the sucker has attached itself to the turtle, a slight pull is given and the startled turtle makes a rush, the line being eased out smartly. Then sport of the kind that a salmon-fisher enjoys when he has hooked a forty-pounder begins. The turtle goes as he pleases; but when he begins to tire, he finds that there is a certain check upon him—slow, steady, never-ceasing. After ten minutes or so a critical phase of the sport occurs. The turtle bobs up to the surface for

a gulp of air, and should he catch sight of the occupants of
the canoe, his start and sudden descent may result in such
a severe tug that the sucker is divorced. But the blacks
watch, and in their experience judge to a nicety when and
where the turtle may rise; telegrams along the line from
the sucker give precise information. They crouch low on
their knees in the canoe as the game emerges with half-shut
eyes and dives again without having ascertained the cause
of the trifling annoyance to which he is being subjected. The
line is shortened up. Perhaps the turtle sulks among the
rocks and coral, and endeavours to free himself from the
sucker by rubbing against the boulders. Knowing all the
wiles and manoeuvres, the blacks play the game accordingly,
and hour after hour may pass, they giving and taking line
with fine skill and the utmost patience. The turtle has become accustomed to the encumbrance, and visits the surface
oftener for air. One of the harpoons is raised, and as the
turtle gleams grey, a couple of fathoms or so under the
water, the canoe is smartly paddled towards the spot whence
it will emerge, and before it can get a mouthful of air the
barbed point, with a strong line attached, is sticking a couple
of inches deep in its shoulder.

"There is a mad splash—a little maelstrom of foam and
ripples, the line runs out to its full length, and the canoe
careers about, accurately steered by the aft man, in the
erratic course of the wounded creature. As it tires, the
heavy shaft of the harpoon secured by the half hitches round
the thin end being a considerable drag, the line is shortened
up, but too much trust is not placed on a single line; some
time may pass before the canoe is brought within striking
distance again. When that moment arrives, a second harpoon is sent into the flesh below the edge of the carapace at
the rear. Unable to break away, the turtle is hauled close

alongside the canoe, secured by the flippers and towed ashore. I have known blacks, after harpooning a turtle, to be towed six miles out to sea before it came their turn to do the towing.

"How they accomplish the feat of securing a turtle that may weigh a couple of hundredweight from a frail bark canoe, in which a white man can scarcely sit and preserve his balance, is astonishing. In a lively sea the blacks sit back, tilting up the stem to meet the coming wave, and then put their weight forward to ease it down, paddling, manoeuvring with the line and bailing all the time. The mere paddling about in the canoe is a feat beyond the dexterity of an ordinary man."

So long as the line is kept taut it is impossible for the sucker-fish to release its hold, and the size of the fish or turtle that can be captured by its means is limited only by the strength of the line and the breaking strain of the fish itself. A turtle weighing forty pounds has been lifted off the ground by gripping a sucker-fish attached to it, and when an attempt was made to pull a fish from the glass side of an aquarium the flesh was heard to crack while the disk still remained firmly adherent. Turtles up to a hundred pounds have been hauled right to the side of the canoe, the blacks displaying a skill and cunning that has probably never been surpassed by the most expert anglers with lines of much greater strength and assisted by elaborate rods and reels.

It is not uncommon when landing a large shark on the Great Barrier Reef to find several sucker-fish attached to its belly or side as it is hauled to the boat, and, although in most cases they release their hold when the shark is lifted out of the water, occasionally they will remain adherent for some time after it is on board.

There is a prevalent impression that the sucker-fish has the extraordinary faculty of guiding the shark to its food-supply, but this has no basis in fact, for the shark is probably at least as capable of locating its food as the sucker. Sharks hunt principally by means of their sense of smell which is much keener than in the bony fishes; they can smell an object in the water at a far greater distance than they or any other fish can see it. Now, the shark's nostrils would guide it to the vicinity of its food long before the food came within the visual range of the sucker-fish, and even though the sucker-fish was actually the first to sight it, the shark would suffer little disadvantage, for its nostrils would indicate the direction in which it lies.

As the shark tears its prey to pieces the sucker-fish swims about picking up the scraps. But in some cases even this is too much trouble for it, and it may actually swim inside the shark's jaws and, attaching itself to the roof of its mouth, obtain its food more directly. It thus may adopt the role of an internal parasite.

If a sucker-fish cannot find a host for its attachment it is forced to forage for itself and this it is well able to do. It frequently takes the bait of anglers fishing on the reef, and it is not uncommon to find it attached to the bottom of a launch where it gathers its food by scavenging amongst the scraps thrown over the side.

ANGLER FISH

An entirely different though equally intriguing method of obtaining food is that adopted by the angler fishes which, although not often taken on the reef, are probably much more common than their capture would appear to signify. They are always too small to take the baits used by anglers and they are rarely taken in nets because they usually lurk in situations where it is impossible to haul a net.

Situated on the top of the head behind the upwardly-directed and capacious mouth is a stiff rod from which dangle one or several appendages that in some species resemble nothing so much as raw meat. The angler, like the stone-fish, squats (no other term so adequately describes its posture) on a rock amidst surroundings which effectively conceal it. A small fish espying in the distance a juicy meal, alive and kicking, rushes towards the lure only to discover too late that it has suddenly vanished, and in an instant it finds itself inside the angler's capacious jaws whence there is no return. The angler, as its prey approaches the lure, quickly drops the rod along its back and with a snap of its jaws engulfs the fish it has so cunningly deceived.

A short while ago there was an angler fish in the Taronga Park (Sydney) aquarium that afforded an ample opportunity of studying the cunning it displayed. In the same tank were many small fishes which the angler fish continually tempted with its lure; its antics were as ludicrous as anything I have ever seen in the realm of natural history. As the fish would approach from its right the rod would be turned towards them and shaken about most vigorously to attract their attention; if they approached from the left the rod would be swung round in that direction. The fish appeared to be frantic in its endeavours to attract, but although I watched it for about half an hour its wares were ignored, possibly because in the confined space of the aquarium the fishes they were intended to lure had had an ample opportunity of watching the fate of their fellows during the period immediately following the angler's introduction into their midst.

It is in the deep, dark abysses that the angler fishes reach their greatest development. There they use a luminous lure to attract their prey, and one species is provided with a stiff rod from the tip of which extends a long line terminating in a three-pronged hook with a light glowing at its base. The compleat angler, indeed.

These "dark unfathom'd caves of ocean" also bear an angler fish extraordinary not only for the disproportion of the sexes but also for the complete degeneracy of the males. The female may reach a length of four feet, but the male when it grows to a length of about four inches attaches itself to a female anywhere on her body by means of its mouth. The tissues of the female break down at the point of attachment and a complete union of the two is formed; the internal organs of the male degenerate with the exception of the reproductive organs, and it becomes entirely dependent on the blood-supply of the female for its nourishment, eventually reaching a stage when it is merely a sac of milt available at the appropriate time for the fertilization of the female's eggs. This "portable bridegroom" becomes, in other words, an external parasite on the female and remains so for the rest of its life.

THE ARCHER FISH

Amongst the curious adaptations that fishes have developed for catching their prey the method adopted by the archer fish is unique. This fish is found in the estuaries of many rivers flowing into the eastern coast of Queensland and, although it does not occur on the reef itself, its method of feeding is of such interest that a moment's digression seems fairly warranted. The fish lurks usually near the bank of a stream in situations where it is overhung with vegetation; here it waits with its upwardly-directed mouth just beneath the surface of the water, and when it sees an insect resting on a branch or hovering in the air above—it spits at it! Out shoots a drop of water with an aim that is uncanny, for the fish has to allow for refraction at the water's sur-

PLATE 34.

SHAWL CRAB

The pattern of the lace-like scroll on the back varies in different
individuals. One-half natural size.

MOTTLED ROCK CRAB

This crab is commonly found hiding under stones along the foreshore
when the tide is out. One-half natural size.

face, and down falls the insect to be immediately gobbled up.

It is possible to keep archer fish in an aquarium by gradually breaking the salt water down to fresh, though it is exceedingly shy and must be handled carefully until it is thoroughly acclimatized. It has been recorded by an aquarist who successfully kept one of these fish for a considerable time that he derived great delight from asking his friends to examine his fish from above; as they peered carefully into the aquarium the fish would almost invariably shoot a drop of water full into a spectator's eye.

"SKIPPERS"

But we must return to the reef. As we pass over its placid waters in a launch it is not an uncommon sight to see the surface broken by numbers of fish which, long and slim, thrust their rigid bodies up till only the tail remains in the water, and, at a slight angle from the vertical, skip over the surface at great speed, the body wriggling from side to side. Thus they continue for a hundred yards or so, their speed gradually diminishing till at length they flop back into the water. These fish, which have received the appropriate name of "skippers," are known elsewhere on the Australian coast as long-toms, and in some parts of the world as needle-fishes; they grow to a length of about three feet and in the distance look like enormous garfish. Their flesh is excellent eating. The skipper is related to the flying fish, and whilst it never completely leaves the water its hurried dancing over the surface is actuated by the same motive, that of escaping from its foes.

THE DEVIL RAY

In striking contrast to these narrow, nimble needle-fish is the huge, flat, and cumbersome devil ray (Plate 30, fig. 1) which on the Great Barrier Reef may reach a width of upwards of fifteen feet and a weight of perhaps a ton. During the winter months till as late as October or November devil rays are common in the central area of the reef and considerable numbers may haunt some of the islands for weeks at a stretch. They swim by means of an up-and-down movement of the great, expansive pectoral fins, or "wings" as they are usually called, and when swimming at the surface their tips may be seen to project at each upward sweep; by tourists these triangular tips are frequently mistaken for the fins of sharks, but the even breaking of the surface in pairs soon dispels the illusion.

Projecting forward from the head are two prominent flexible "horns," which are really modified fins; they apparently assist in some way in gathering up the food which consists of small forms of animal life. There are an enormous number of minute teeth in the lower jaw and an apparatus for sifting the food in the throat just in front of the gill-slits. The mouth is a great horizontal opening extending between the bases of the two horns; it is therefore situated in front of the head, whereas in the smaller horned or ox rays, also common in the Barrier Reef area, it lies underneath (Plate 30, fig. 2) as in ordinary rays and most sharks. The horned ray is characterized, also, by the possession of teeth in both jaws.

Although the devil ray will not take a bait it provides tourists with some excitement when harpooned for it may tow a launch about for hours before becoming exhausted.

The devil ray is perfectly harmless; it does not even possess a barbed spine on its tail as in most of our sting-rays; but it was held in great dread by the ancients who were under the impression that it would wrap its fins round a man and squeeze him to death.

JUMPING BLENNIES

Hiding under stones when the tide is out a curious fish known as a blenny is found on many of the Barrier Reef islands; this blenny grows to a length of six or seven inches and, like the mud-skipper, it can live out of water for long periods though it is never found anywhere except under stones where there is always a considerable amount of moisture. Immediately one of these stones is lifted the fish hop in all directions like a lot of elongated fleas and, quickly recovering from their initial fright, scamper towards the water.

STRIPED CATFISH

Occasionally as you row over the reef you may be mystified by a dark, greenish-black mass in the water which, without well-defined shape, moves slowly along, now turning a little this way, now that; peer as closely as you like and you will find it impossible to determine what it is. It is obviously alive, but its shapelessness gives no clue to its identity. If, however, you procure a landing-net and dip it quickly into the mass you will find your net wriggling with elongated fish, each about a foot long, black on the back with two longitudinal white stripes on the sides. They are striped catfish; but you will do well to handle them carefully for they have spines in their fins which can inflict a nasty wound. So closely packed do they swim that it is impossible to distinguish the individual fish in a shoal as it rolls along over the reef like a sluggishly animated ball.

Similar dense masses of fishes known as hardyheads occur very commonly round several islands of the Capricorn Group, but in their case the shoals usually remain as stationary as a rock for hours at a stretch.

REEF EELS

Eels of several species are common objects amongst the coral; some of them are very beautiful (Plate 40), at least they are very beautifully mottled with a wide range of pleasing colours, though their snake-like movements cause an involuntary revulsion as they wriggle about the reef. They usually lie twined amongst the crevices of the coral and are very difficult to capture for they quickly retract when approached and squirm from hole to hole in the irregular masses of coral. Some grow to a large size and are very powerful; incidentally, also, they may be very vicious and are capable of biting savagely.

BOX-FISH AND COW-FISH

No discussion of the curious life of the reef would be complete without reference to the armour-plated curiosities known as box-fish and their close relatives the cow-fish. Beneath the skin, which is usually a mottled brown, a bony skeleton forms a rigid box-like covering for the internal organs; the armour does not form a complete enclosure, however, for openings occur in it to give play to the fins and tail. The box-fish is one of the commonest species on the reef flat right throughout the length of the Barrier, and it cuts a curious figure as the vigorous movements of its tail propel it slowly away.

The cow-fish is similarly armed, but in addition it has a pair of horns projecting well forward above the eyes and a similar pair pointing backwards near the tail, seemingly ready to ram fore or aft.

TOAD-FISH AND PORCUPINE-FISH

Related to the box-fishes are the bizarre toad-fish and porcupine-fish which are also plentiful and widely distributed over the reef; their chief interest lies in their power to

PLATE 35.

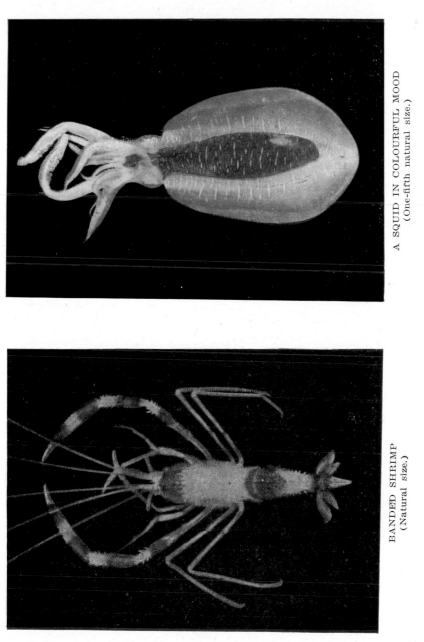

A SQUID IN COLOURFUL MOOD
(One-fifth natural size.)

BANDED SHRIMP
(Natural size.)

inflate themselves with either water or air till they assume an almost globular shape, the spines of the porcupine-fish then standing erect and rigid, forming a most effective defensive armature. Their teeth are united into a stout beaklike structure, strong and powerful, which enables the fish to bite off pieces of coral and similar hard substances which they seek as food. The flesh of both the toad-fish and the porcupine-fish is poisonous.

ORNATE SHARKS

In addition to the large predacious sharks to which reference is made in Chapter XVII, there are several smaller species that abound on the reef and are of considerable interest. The wobbegong and the closely related species, the carpet-shark, are frequently found in coral pools when the tide is out. Both are very sluggish and are decorated with complex patterns of brown and violet which have been likened to the handsome design of a carpet or rug, but their mouths are rendered repulsive by a fringe of irregular outgrowths of skin. The wobbegong and carpet-sharks grow to a length of about six or seven feet; neither is regarded as dangerous, though if trodden on it is likely to snap at one's leg with painful consequences.

Another small species that grows to a length of about three feet only is the spotted cat-shark, which is frequently seen groping its way in a half-blind fashion in coral pools; it is irregularly covered with diffuse spots, but one on each side behind the pectoral fin is larger and much more conspicuous than the others; it is surrounded by a white band which gives it the appearance of a huge eye on the side of the body. It is perfectly harmless.

M

CHAPTER
THIRTEEN

*Introducing
the Mermaid*

THE mermaid has existed in man's fancy ever since he
went down to the sea in ships. Most old-world countries have their own legends concerning it, and always it is
pictured as a maiden of great beauty down to the waist,
with the lower half of the body covered with scales and
tapering to a fish's tail.

Amongst the ancient Greeks and Romans mermaids were
known as sirens or nereids, and there can be no doubt that
many people had implicit faith in their reality. Associated
with them was a dread of their enchantment, for their be-
witching spell presaged disaster. Despite their exceeding
beauty and apparent happiness as they swam gracefully in
the sea or rested on moss-covered rocks the gloom of sad-
ness hung over their comely heads.

Pliny, the great Roman naturalist, certainly gave credence
to their existence for he wrote: "Nor yet is the figure generally attributed to the nereids at all a fiction; only in them,
the portion of the body that resembles the human figure
is still rough all over with scales. For one of these figures
was seen upon the same shores, and as it died, its plaintive
murmurs were heard by the inhabitants at a distance."

While the spell of the sirens was fatal to humans, it was
believed that if any sailor could resist their allurements the
sirens themselves were sure to die, and Greek mythology has
enriched us with the imperishable story of Ulysses' defiance.

Stopping the ears of his sailors with wax and lashing himself to the mast, he succeeded in sailing beyond the spell of their enchanting songs.

Credence was given by many western Europeans to the mermaid, as it was also to the sea-serpent, until quite modern times, and many were the enchanting tales, told with a wealth of colour and detail, of intriguing love-affairs with these beautiful maidens.

Is it possible that such widespread belief in the mermaid can have some basis in fact? It is generally conceded that it has; that the dugong, seen by sailors languishing in a tropical sea on a moonlight night, perhaps clasping a baby to its breast, has run riot with the imagination of the more impressionable of them and inspired their tales of love and beauty on their return to port. In extenuation it must be remembered that in those days of slow sailing ships the sailors were a long time away from home. But even so a glance at the dugong's face, illustrated in Plate 31, fig. 2, would indicate that these adventurers were gifted with an imagination quite beyond the ordinary, for the face of the dugong is calculated to dispel the ardour of the most love-sick seaman—at least, when the sun rises in the morning.

Even in science the recognition of the fanciful resemblance of the dugong to the siren has been perpetuated by the name *Sirenia* being given to the order of dugongs and their relatives, the manatees.

The name "dugong" is derived from the Malayan word *duyong*. It is, of course, a mammal and, like the whale, is descended from ancestors which in the long ago lived entirely on land but which reverted back to the water whence all land animals originally sprang. Its nearest present-day relatives are not whales, however, but elephants!

The dugong may be found throughout the whole length

and breadth of the Great Barrier Reef, where it is usually known as—a siren? a nereid? a sea-nymph? None of these; it passes under the matter-of-fact name of "sea-cow." Is our romance altogether dead?

It ranges from Moreton Bay on the southern Queensland coast round the northern and western coasts of Australia as far south as Broome in Western Australia, and is probably most abundant round the islands of Torres Strait. At one time its range extended much farther south as indicated by the fact that its bones have been found in Botany Bay in New South Wales. Beyond Australian waters it occurs in the Red Sea, along the shores of the Indian Ocean and the Philippines.

The dugong grows to a length of about nine feet and may weigh upwards of half a ton; its colour varies from a reddish-grey to olive green; it swims by means of the powerful horizontal tail, possibly aided at times by the pair of flippers that spring from the shoulders and correspond with the fore-limbs of land mammals; of the hind limbs there is no external trace. Although it may be found leading a solitary existence it more commonly associates in herds, and even to-day when its ranks have been sadly thinned as many as forty or more may be seen in a single herd. Unfortunately, such numbers are not now common for great toll has been taken of them for their oil, flesh, and hide.

Like other mammals that have taken to an aquatic life, the dugong breathes air and must come to the surface to obtain it. Its lungs are very capacious and it can stay below for quite considerable periods; its nostrils, which are situated above the muzzle, are provided with valves which prevent the ingress of water during submergence.

The dugong is sluggish and perfectly harmless; it is completely vegetarian in its diet and loves lazily to browse on

PLATE 36.

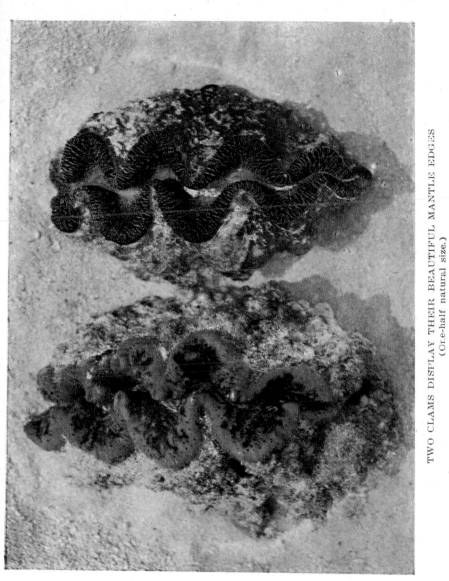

TWO CLAMS DISPLAY THEIR BEAUTIFUL MANTLE EDGES
(One-half natural size.)

sea-grass (*Cymodocea*) common in the shallow water of the tropics. It seizes the blades of grass principally by means of the upper lip which is in the form of a blunt muzzle divided by a median groove into swollen pads covered with stiff bristles. The plants are grasped by the opening and closing of the pads and are then conducted to the mouth by a backward movement of the muzzle. They are crushed between horny plates situated in both upper and lower jaws and then ground between a series of molar teeth. The adult male develops a pair of ivory tusks which may attain a length of nine inches; it is thought that these may assist in feeding, perhaps by the rooting up of the grass, though it seems scarcely fair that the male alone should possess this advantage.

One baby is produced at birth though it is possible that on rare occasions twins are found; when newly born the young one measures about three feet in length, and it is hugged affectionately to the mother's side by means of one of the flippers; its milk is obtained, of course, from the mammary glands of the parent, which are situated between the flippers. When the mother rises to the surface to breathe she takes care to see that the nostrils of the baby are also exposed.

The dugong seems to be capable of a real affection, not only for its young, but also for its fellows. Evidence of this has been given by Banfield in his *Confessions of a Beach-comber*. "Rolling and lurching along," he states, "gambolling like good-humoured, contented children, the herd moves leisurely to and from favourite feeding-grounds, occasionally splashing mightily with powerful tails to make fountains of illuminated spray—great, unreflecting, sportful water-babes. Admiration is enhanced as one learns of the affection of the dugong for its young and its love for the companionship of its fellows. When one of a pair is killed, the other haunts the locality for days. Its suspirations seem sighs, and its presence melancholy proof of the reality of its bereavement."

The dugong has always been a favourite food of the Australian aboriginal and its capture by means of a spear or harpoon (Plate 31, fig. 1) called for a combination of skill and ingenuity. But we shall let Banfield describe this for us also. "Blacks harpoon dugong as they do turtle," he writes, "but the sport demands greater patience and dexterity, for the dugong is a wary animal and shy, to be approached only with the exercise of artful caution. An inadvertent splash of the paddle or a miss with the harpoon, and the game is away with a torpedo-like swirl. To be successful in the sport the black must be familiar with the life-history of the creature to a certain extent—understanding its peregrinations and the reason for them—the strength and trend of currents and the locality of favourite feeding-grounds. Fragments of floating grass sometimes tell where the animal is feeding. An oily appearance on the surface of the sea shows its course, and if the wind sits in the right quarter the keen-scented black detects its presence when the animal has risen to breathe at a point invisible to him.

"Using a barbless point attached to a long and strong line, and fitted into a socket in the heavy end of the harpoon shaft, the black waits and watches. With the utmost caution, and in absolute silence, he follows in his canoe the dugong as it feeds, and strikes as it rises to breathe. A mad splash, a wild rush! The canoe bounces over the water as the line tightens. Its occupant sits back and steers with flippers of bark, until as the game weakens he is able to approach and plunge another harpoon into it. Sometimes the end of the line is made fast to a buoy of light wood, which the creature tows till exhausted.

"It is stated that the blacks towards Cape York, having secured the animal with a line attached to a dart insufficient in length to penetrate the hide and the true skin, seize it by the nose, and plug the nostrils with their fingers until it drowns. Here, too, the natives have discovered that the nose is the vulnerable part of the dugong, and having first harpooned it in any part of the body, await an opportunity of spearing it there, with almost invariably speedy fatal effects."

The Torres Strait islanders erect a high staging with a platform at the top for the harpooning of dugongs. Careful note is kept, during the course of their wanderings over the reef, of fragments of dugong grass which might indicate where the animals have been browsing, and the staging is erected there in the expectation that they will return at night to the same pasture. Should they do so they are harpooned from this vantage-point. The harpoon used by these blacks consists of a small shaft tipped with a bone barb and attached to a coil of rope; the shaft fits loosely into a heavy spear about fifteen feet long, and when the dugong is struck the harpoon is freed from the spear.

The weapons of the blacks are primitive yet efficient in their hands, and although they have taken toll of great numbers through the ages, dugongs were plentiful enough when white men came on the scene. As late as 1893 a herd was recorded in Moreton Bay extending over a length of nearly three miles with a width of about three hundred yards. At a later date extravagant claims were made concerning the medicinal quality of the oil yielded by the dugong's blubber and high prices, which ranged up to £3 per gallon, were obtained for it. This, of course, led to a wholesale slaughter which made great inroads on the available supplies. The reputation of the oil has since declined considerably, but even to-day small quantities are on the market.

In addition to the oil, the hide, which is nearly an inch thick, was tanned, and considerable quantities of flesh, parts of which resemble pork or veal, were eaten.

Now, if the slaughter of dugongs is allowed to continue unchecked, it is inevitable that with the use of modern and efficient nets their systematic pursuit will reduce them to the point of extinction, and every effort must be made to see that this does not occur, for the dugong has a very great scientific interest and is one of the most harmless creatures in the sea.

And our sailors will be robbed of a most valuable source of inspiration.

IN Chapter II we referred to the dominant types of trees that vegetate a coral island, in some parts so thickly that they may form an impenetrable jungle. Some of these trees deserve more than a passing mention, while others, more sparsely distributed, possess features that give them a singular interest.

On many islands papaws flourish. Now, this tree bears a luscious fruit which may attain a weight of over eight pounds; its worth has been extolled in many countries but it is doubtful whether it has ever had a greater admirer than our friend Banfield, of beachcombing fame. Listen to what he says of its virtues:

"Ripened in ample light, with abundance of water, and in high temperature, the fruit must not be torn from the tree 'with forced fingers rude,' lest the abbreviated stalk pulls out a jagged plug, leaving a hole for the untimely air to enter. The stalk must be carefully cut, and the spice-exhaling fruit borne reverently and immediately to the table. The rite is to be performed in the cool of the morning, for the papaw is essentially a breakfast fruit, and then when the knife slides into the buff-coloured flesh of a cheesy consistency, minute colourless globules exude from the facets of the slices. These glistening beads are emblems of perfection. Plentiful dark seeds adhere to the interior surface. Some take their papaw with the merest sensation of salt, some with sugar and a drop or two of lime or lemon juice;

some with a few of the seeds, which have the flavour of nas-
turtium. The wise eat it with silent praise. In certain obvious
respects it has no equal. It is so clean; it conveys a delicate
perception of musk—sweet, not florid; soft, soothing, and
singularly persuasive. It does not cloy the palate, but rather
seductively stimulates the appetite. Its effect is immediately
comforting, for to the stomach it is pleasant, wholesome, and
helpful. When you have eaten of a papaw in its prime, one
that has grown without check or hindrance, and has been
removed from the tree without bruise or blemish, you have
within you pure, good and chaste food, and you should be
thankful and of gladsome mind. Moreover, no untoward
effects arise from excess of appetite. If you be of the fair
sex your eyes may brighten on such diet, and your com-
plexion become more radiant. If a mere man, you will be
the manlier."

Obviously, Banfield loved his papaws. I know of no other
fruit that has called forth such extravagant language;
indeed, I can recollect no food for which such wonderful properties have been claimed. Yes, I can—the oyster. This
great delicacy has a far more ancient history and its praises
have been sung from very early times. For instance, Pliny
the elder, in the first century of the Christian era, made the
following claims for its beneficial effect on many of our
bodily ailments:

"We will take the present opportunity of stating all the
medicinal properties that are attributed to oysters. They are
singularly refreshing to the stomach, and tend to restore the
appetite. Oysters are slightly laxative to the bowels; and
boiled in honied wine, they relieve tenesmus, in cases where
it is unattended with ulceration. They act detergently also
upon ulcerations of the bladder. Boiled in their shells,
unopened just as they come to hand, oysters are marvel-

lously efficacious for rheumatic defluxions. Calcined oyster-shells, mixed with honey, allay affections of the uvula and of the tonsillary glands: they are similarly used for impos-thumes of the parotid glands, inflamed tumours, and indura-tions of the mamillae. Applied with water, these ashes are good for ulcerations of the head, and impart a plumpness to the skin in females. They are sprinkled, too, upon burns, and are highly esteemed as a dentifrice. Applied with vine-gar, they are good for the removal of prurigo and of pituit-ous eruptions. Beaten up in a raw state, they are curative of scrofula and of chilblains upon the feet."

But it is not quite fair to compare the advocacy of an ancient with that of a modern writer. Nor is it necessary, for the English language has been strained to its utmost ade-quately to describe the oyster's merits. Has not the use of the term "succulent bivalve" been so hackneyed that it is now taboo? Harken to its virtues as portrayed by an anonymous writer of the middle of the eighteenth century:

"The Oyster! The mere writing of the word creates sen-sations of succulence—gastronomical pleasures, nutritive food, easy digestion, palatable indulgence—then go sleep in peace! True, true, oh oyster! thou art the best beloved of the loved!

"It contains much nutritive substance, which is very diges-tive, and produces a peculiar charm and an inexplicable plea-sure. After having eaten oysters we feel joyous, light, and agreeable—yes, one might say, fabulously well. He who has eaten oysters for the first time is best enabled to judge of this; for, soon after having eaten them, he will experience a sensation he never felt before, and never had an idea of."

Just as obviously, this author loved his oysters. The papaw and the oyster are food for the gods, indeed. The reader is left to make his choice. Personally, while agreeing with much that Banfield says about the papaw, I prefer the oyster.

The papaw has one unique quality, however; it possesses the extraordinary property of rendering tough meat tender. This is no extravagant claim, no medieval superstition; it has been demonstrated far too often for that. Place tough meat in contact with the cut flesh of the papaw, or wrap the leaves of the tree round it even, and the meat will become almost unbelievably tender. An investigation of the cause of this curious property revealed the presence of a ferment known as papain, which possesses the power of digesting meat. Not only this; the papaw has been used extensively and with considerable success in medicine for the treatment of dyspepsia.

What has the oyster to say to that? I can hear it reminding me that it possesses certain stimulating qualities of far greater value. Perhaps we had better leave them to argue it out for we must continue our wanderings.

THE PANDANUS-TREE AND ITS FRUIT

Approaching a group of Pandanus-trees we see what appear in the distance to be large pineapples suspended from their branches. Examining them more closely we find the resemblance to be a superficial one only, but it has been responsible for the name "screw-pine" being frequently applied to the tree, the term "screw" being derived from the arrangement of the leaves in a series of spirals to form tufts at the ends of the branches. Reference to Plate 45 will give a clearer conception of its shape, colour, and structure than any words of mine can convey; the fruit there illustrated measured ten inches in length.

The fruit of the Pandanus-tree is often referred to in northern Australia as "bread-fruit" because of the fact that the aborigines frequently pounded it to make a "bread" of dough-like consistency. If opened when ripe it is found

PLATE 37.

THE EXPOSED MANTLES OF CLAMS DISPLAY A WIDE RANGE OF COLOUR VARIATION

to possess a pleasant aroma, while internally the fruit is fibrous, starchy, and glutinous with a core of similar character, and a flavour that is rather sweet but very cloying to the palate.

The stilt-like roots (Plate 41) provide wonderful support for a tree that has been destined to grow in situations where the sand, liable to be moved by the wind or undermined by the sea, would prove far too unstable to provide a secure hold for roots of more normal form and disposition.

MANGROVES

The development of this type of root is seen at its best in several species of mangroves which occur prolifically on those islands where mud has accumulated. These mangroves are always associated with muddy areas and are rarely found in the lower half of the reef where it diverges far away from the coast and is therefore not susceptible to deposits of mud brought down by coastal streams during floods. In the northern area, although they are never found on the Barrier itself on account of the wash of the surf, they grow profusely on many of the coral islands situated between it and the mainland.

The largest and commonest in this region is a tree known as the red mangrove, which may attain a height of fifty or sixty feet. It gives the impression that it has been pulled well out of the mud for the trunk may begin some feet above it, and the roots, which in most other trees are embedded beneath the soil, spread out and arch and branch to form a complicated network covering an area of many square yards. In a dense forest of such trees progress is impossible. The black, oozy, foul mud in which the mangroves grow does not supply sufficient aeration for the roots that penetrate it and the stilt-roots, exposed to the air at low tide, assist in this function, aided by aerial roots which grow downwards from the branches and sometimes enter the mud. But the spreading stilt-roots serve another important purpose—they act as highly efficient anchorages in the soft mud while yet they do not present an expansive surface to the destructive force of the sea when the tide is high and the wind blows strongly.

The long and narrow spindle-shaped seeds, unlike those of most other plants, which cannot develop unless embedded in soil, germinate on the tree and may attain a length of three or four feet; they eventually drop in the form of embryo plants and, if the tide is out, stick into the mud; in a very short time roots develop, and leaves shoot out from the free end. If, however, they should happen to fall from the parent tree when the tide is high they float at the surface in a vertical position and are carried away by the current. In this condition they will live for a long time and may eventually be deposited on mud, scores, perhaps hundreds, of miles from their original location. Thus is barren mud vegetated.

There are two or three other widely distributed species of mangroves that possess roots of a somewhat similar type and all perform a very important role by assisting the accumulation of mud and by collecting debris which helps to consolidate it. As the mud settles on the bottom it gradually becomes more and more elevated till it reaches a height where conditions are no longer favourable to the growth of the tree, which is thus killed by a condition it has itself very largely been responsible for. But it has paved the way for an invasion of other plants unfitted for a life in the salt ooze which the mangrove found so completely to its liking.

Of a very different type is the white mangrove, which may attain a height of about thirty feet. This tree has many features of interest but we must content ourselves with the consideration of one or two only. From its roots, which spread widely beneath the surface of the mud, great numbers of accessory breathing-roots project into the air; they grow to a length of eight or nine inches and resemble the young shoots of asparagus thrusting their heads through the mud, though they are more usually referred to as "cobbler's-pegs." These, too, are an important agency in the accumulation of debris, and they frequently bear great crops of oysters. On the coast of New South Wales I have seen mud-flats so densely crowded with these projecting roots, each bearing up to a dozen oysters, that it was impossible to walk over them without crunching them down at every step. The shells of many succeeding generations of oysters help materially to bind and consolidate the mud.

The timber of the white mangrove is peculiar in the arrangement of the annual rings; the fibres of each layer are disposed in a different direction from those with which it is in contact, forming a sort of plywood which adds greatly to its strength—a rather necessary quality in a tree that has a habit of leaning at the most acute angles.

Much has been written about the ugliness of a mangrove swamp. Seen at a distance when the tide is high a mangrove forest may be very beautiful, forming a dense shining hedge between the land and the water, but to walk through it when the tide is low, sinking deep in the soft mud, is an experience which leaves few happy memories, though the crab life that usually abounds in such situations compensates in its interest for all the labour expended. But crabs are another story.

Such are some of the highlights of the vegetation of the coral islands of the Great Barrier Reef. On the mainland islands we find a vegetation which for the most part is very dissimilar. These islands, as we have seen, once formed part of the mainland, and the trees and shrubs that clothe them are those characteristic of the coastal belt, though many of them have a mangrove flora similar in all respects to that found on some of the true coral islands. Eucalypts, acacias, pines, casuarinas, and scores of others, whose real home is on the mainland, cover these islands in dense forests, but we need not linger over them here.

THE INDUSTRIOUS GREEN TREE-ANT

Continuing our exploration we come across a mass of tangled leaves united at their edges to form a bundle perhaps as big as a football (Plate 32, fig. 1). We have called at the residence of one of the most amazing insects in the world, the green tree-ant. For pugnacity, for tenacity, for industry, for the development of instincts which superficially convey the impression that we are dealing with the most intelligent of all the lower animals, this handsome vivid green ant probably holds pride of place.

"Hell has no fury like a woman scorned," wrote Congreve early in the seventeenth century. The green tree-ant was obviously not known then. But, if you would care for a little first-hand knowledge, knock on its front door and judge for yourself the welcome you receive. One after another they will dash out, one after another they will fall on you, on your neck, on your head, on your hands, and with a vicious jab bury their jaws up to the hilt—and stay there. If a bulldog gets his teeth into you, you at least have a chance to wrench free, but the green tree-ant will not let go; you can pull its body from its head but its jaws will remain embedded in your flesh.

Why all this fury? What is there about its home that it takes such pains to protect it?

If you are patient—and careful—you may be fortunate enough to see this industrious creature at work. It has eggs and young ones to protect; it must make them snug and comfortable, and provide them with shelter from the rain, and it accomplishes this by joining many leaves together at their

PLATE 38.

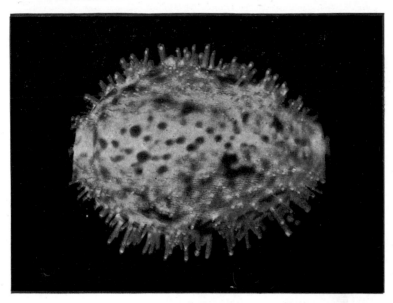

TIGER COWRIE

The extended mantles almost completely cover the shell. Three-quarters natural size.

MUTTON-FISH

A mollusc whose shell covers portion only of its body. Two-thirds natural size.

edges. This it does in a most extraordinary manner. A close examination of the nest will reveal that the leaves are all firmly bound with a fine but strong silk. But these ants are unable to produce silk. Whence then do they obtain it? From the babies, which they use as a weaver uses a shuttle.

When active nest-building operations are in progress, a whole army of ants will line up on the edge of a leaf and, gripping it securely with their legs, stretch up and seize another leaf in their jaws; all heave together and draw the leaf down till it is close to the one they are standing on. Other workers rush to the nursery, grab the young ones round the middle with their mouths pointing forward, and hasten to the field of operations. Now, these larvae were

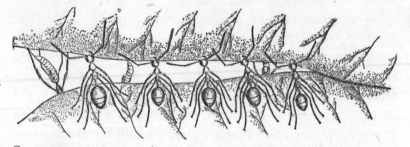

Green tree-ants drawing the edges of two leaves together while others cement them by means of a silky secretion produced by the larval ants.
—After DOFLEIN.

ready to secrete from their mouths a sticky fluid which hardens on exposure to air and is woven into a silky cocoon; in this they would lie till they were ready to develop into adult ants. But the secretion is valuable to the community for other purposes. The adult ants jab the mouths of the babies against the edge of the upper leaf then against the lower leaf, uniting the two by a silky thread; again and again they thrust the baby upward and downward to weave a fine web which forms a union between the two leaves.

When this living shuttle is exhausted of its supplies, the

N

ant rushes back to the nursery, dumps it down without ceremony, and grabbing another, returns to its task, using baby
after baby till the job is completed.

If the drawing of the leaves together were confined to
those within reach of an individual ant, it would only be in
the most fortuitous circumstances that leaves close enough
for the purpose could be secured. But we find many in the
nest that have clearly been drawn from a much greater distance than this. How, then, have they managed this extraordinary feat? The ants form living chains or hauling ropes.
When the leaf required is well out of reach the ants gather
on the surface of the upper one and one of them grips the
edge with its jaws and hangs suspended; immediately a
second ant climbs over its body and, gripping it round the
waist, hangs on; a third, a fourth, a fifth, perhaps a sixth ant
climbs down till the other leaf is reached. Meanwhile, similar chains have formed elsewhere between the leaves and
they are used as bridges by other ants which desire to pass
from leaf to leaf. When sufficient chains are in position the
ants pull and heave in unison, exerting every atom of their
strength, till the two edges are close enough for the army of
weavers, waiting on the leaf below, to do their stitching.

During a recent visit to Hayman Island I was watching
the formation of these chains as the edges of two leaves were
being brought into close apposition when the ants holding
the lower leaf lost their foothold and the leaves sprang apart
to a distance of two and a half inches. Each of the ant chains
necessary to bridge this gap initially must have comprised
from eight to ten individuals.

If the leaves are large fewer are necessary, but the work
is heavier, and if they are small hundreds may be required to
build a nest large enough for the thousands of ants that
require shelter within. But the work is not finished when the
leaves are united externally. Galleries and chambers are

constructed inside, supported by pillars and beams of the same tough, silky material.

Truly this ant is one of the wonders of a race which is full of surprises. But its industry is not confined to nest-building. It also runs a dairy! It tenders with great care flocks of aphids, scale insects or mealy bugs, which secrete honey-dew as they feed on the leaves of trees, and it induces the aphids to secrete this great delicacy in abundance by gently stroking their backs with its antennae! If the herd shows a tendency to roam too far afield the grubs are again requisitioned and made to spin a web about them as they feed so that the ants will always know where they are to be found (Plate 32, fig. 2); for just the same reason, indeed, as the herdsman builds a fence around his flock.

Undeterred by their pugnacity, the aborigines of northern Queensland relished these ants as food, the larvae particularly being considered a great delicacy. Sometimes they would cut away the branch that supported the nest and shake it vigorously to rid it of the ants, leaving the helpless larvae at their mercy; or they would smoke the ants out; or, perhaps, throw the nest into water when the adults would swim for land. The larvae or grubs were eaten raw, sometimes after rolling them into a ball between the palms of the hands. Nor were the adult ants always wasted. On occasion they were mashed up in water to form an acid drink which was held in high esteem; indeed, strange as it may seem, this cordial has also been relished by many white people.

The green tree-ant is a common object on many of the islands of the Great Barrier Reef and it appears to be quite indifferent to the kind of tree it chooses for its nest.

AN ANGLING SPIDER

When our modern Isaac Walton goes fishing he chooses carefully the size of hook he intends to use according to the sort of fish he expects to catch; he baits it carefully and lets down his line; presently, feeling a nibble, he strikes—and usually misses. Nibble after nibble accounts for bait after bait and, his patience finally exhausted, he decides to repair to the tavern. Possibly he was not skilled in the gentle art, or perhaps his hook was too large for the fish that happened to be about at the time. I wonder what this angler would say if he were offered a bait which not only attracted fish from far and near, but so tenaciously stuck to them as soon as they touched it that they could be hauled in without a chance of escape? Of course, he wouldn't believe it, and we certainly could not offer him such a wonderful lure, but there is a spider occasionally found on some of the islands of the Great Barrier Reef which fishes in just that manner.

This spider, which goes under the name of the "Queen of Spinners," or the "Magnificent Spider," spins at night a tight-rope between two branches of a tree and from this it hangs suspended. It then lets down a fine but strong thread at the end of which is an extremely sticky globule with perhaps one or two smaller ones a little higher on the line. Holding the line with one of its front legs the spider waits and watches, and it usually has not long to wait for there appears to be some irresistible attraction for certain moths in that lure; one comes fluttering along and at its approach the spider whirls the line and the bait most frantically. It is difficult to say what the object of this actually is, though perhaps the moth, like many fish, prefers a moving bait; whatever the reason, it appears to be an essential part of the sport; it proves too strong a lure, the moth touches it and—sticks fast.

As soon as the moth is trapped the spider hauls up its line, injects a drop of deadly venom, tidily binds its prey into a compact bundle and quietly proceeds to suck out its nourishment; or if it is feeling particularly hungry it may place it on one side, rebait its line, and continue its fishing.

PLATE 39.

A BEAUTIFUL SEA-SLUG OR NUDIBRANCH COMMON ON THE REEF
(Natural size.)

The spider is a handsome creature, at least it is nicely mottled and spotted on a delicate cream ground, but it is rather too prominent about the abdomen to be a perfect figure; in fact, it is nearly all abdomen which is fully twenty times larger than its head and thorax combined. It measures about three-quarters of an inch in length (or should we say diameter?), and probably would be rarely found if it were not for the prominent cocoons it spins. These are spindle-shaped structures three or four inches long and about an inch in diameter across the middle; they are attached to the leaves and branches of trees from which they hang suspended. Inside this outer covering, which has the texture of tissue paper but is far stronger, there is a smaller cocoon in which the eggs are laid and between the two there is a mass of loose fibres, which form a perfect cushion.

About three months after the eggs are laid the young spiders hatch out, and proceeding at once to bore their way through the envelope, they spin fine silken threads and float away on the breeze.

As many as six of these cocoons may be constructed by a single female in one breeding-season, and each of them may contain from four hundred to six hundred eggs. Apparently the spider is a better angler than a parachutist for it appears to be nowhere very common.

THE ANT-LION AND ITS CUNNING TRAP

A common but inconspicuous inhabitant of many coral islands is the ant-lion, which vies with the angling spider in the trap it sets to catch its prey.

If you search the coral sand in situations fairly well protected from the weather you may see numbers of cone-shaped depressions with steep sides, an inch or two in diameter at the top and about an inch deep. Then, if you are of a patient disposition, you may feel inclined to make yourself comfortable beside them and watch for ants strolling about that way. Presently an ant may come along and step on the edge of the pit; the sand is loose and the sides are steep, and the ant stumbles and struggles to right itself. This is found to be no easy matter for it finds that showers of loose sand are falling all around it; a miniature volcano has broken out at the bottom of the pit and clouds of sand belch forth and fall down the sides. On a steep slope that is continually giving way beneath its feet the ant has little chance; in spite of its desperate struggles it falls to the bottom and two strong nippers, inwardly curved to sharp points, grip it as in a vice and drag it to its doom.

If, now, you thrust the blade of a pocket-knife quickly beneath the sand at the bottom of the pit and do a little scooping yourself you will find a small segmented creature, drab, wrinkled, ugly, about half an inch long and armed with a pair of nippers that may measure a third of the length of its body. You have unearthed an ant-lion. Incidentally, you have saved the ant's life, for once caught in the ant-lion's jaws it has no chance of escape; these jaws are pierced right to their tips and serve to suck the blood of its victims.

When the ant-lion is fully grown it changes to a pupa and lies dormant for a considerable time, later to burst forth as a delicate insect with a long, slender body and wings that resemble the finest of gauze. It is now as beautiful as originally it was ugly; no longer does it construct a cunning trap but flutters about in the sunlight in search of a mate. I often wonder whether this delicate and handsome creature, once an ugly and ruthless marauder, remembers the murderous days of its youth.

ANGLERS on the Great Barrier Reef fall naturally into two classes. There are those who regard angling only as a side-line; who join a boat party bent on reef fishing because it is one of the things usually done on the reef; it is part of the programme and one must see and do everything possible in the limited time available. When preparing for the trip these novices in the noble art usually go to a fishing-tackle dealer and seek his advice as to the tackle required, but many rely on the skipper of the boat for their gear.

Then we have the real anglers who fish for the surface-swimming fish with rods and gear of the utmost refinement. There is nothing casual about these anglers; fishing is in their blood and years of experience have taught them how to match their skill against the cunning and fierce fury of the fastest of the ocean's denizens. For months before the trip they have discussed together the habits of the different species, for months they have argued about the respective merits of the various types of gear—the best kind of rod, the efficiency of reels, the breaking strain of lines, and the attraction of lures. To these men angling is a life's hobby; they talk eternally of the catches of the past, they dream of the greater ones to come.

We join a launch party about to start for a day's angling for fish that live amongst and in the vicinity of the coral at Heron Island. The skipper knows the best spots, and as he makes for a likely ground we rig our lines, some of heavy cord, others of gut, the skipper supplying sinkers and hooks if those we have come provided with are not of the right weight and size. A spot is chosen where there is a long, wide channel between coral reefs; the engine stops and the launch is left to drift along where the bottom is broken only by isolated coral boulders. The lines are baited with large pieces of fish caught the previous day, and over they go, the heavy sinkers taking them rapidly to the bottom.

Within a few minutes one of the party is hauling in the first fish. Quietly but with obvious pride (for the competition for the first fish is always keen) he pulls in his line while all the other anglers peer into the water in an endeavour to catch a glimpse of the fish as it nears the surface. Shortly a coral bream of glistening silver is flopping on the deck; it weighs about three pounds and, as the skipper approaches, the angler responsible for it holds up his prize for inspection. Never shall I forget the look in this man's face as the skipper takes his catch with the casual remark that such small fish "come in handy for bait." What sacrilege! Our friend's previous angling experience had been obtained in waters where a three-pound bream would be regarded as a rare prize, a fish to be talked about for long afterwards. And here it is regarded as rubbish, fit only for use as bait. But if a three-pound fish is so despised there must be something worth-while in store for us. And there was.

Suddenly one of the anglers is hauling in a fish that is obviously heavy; although he knows he must get it into the boat as quickly as possible lest it take his line amongst the coral, which will surely cut it, he is several times forced to let it run a short distance before he is able again to turn it. Nearer and nearer he brings his catch till just beneath the surface we see a handsome fellow flashing pink and silvery;

a final dash and it disappears beneath the blue water; slowly it is again brought to the surface, this time to be hastily lifted into the boat where it is determined as a king snapper of about fifteen pounds, its silvery sides ornamented with bright pink bands which take the form of a broad arrow and have been responsible for the name "Government bream" being sometimes bestowed upon it (Plate 47, fig. 2). "That's better," remarks our skipper as he places the fish in the ice-box, "we shall probably get a lot of these this morning."

Now we are properly amongst the fish; they are flopping everywhere on the deck. And what fish! Every one is an object of great beauty—coral cod up to thirty pounds, no two alike in colour, some bright red spotted with blue, others blue with red spots; snapper, a delicate pink with a flashing iridescence; red-mouthed emperors bluish-silver with blood-red markings about the head and on the dorsal fin and the bases of the pectorals (Plate 48, fig. 2); hussars, pale pink with a broad greenish-yellow band traversing the sides longitudinally; blue-spotted groper in a variety of beautiful liveries, some green along the back with blue fins and pale pink sides (Plate 48, fig. 1); others bright pink with multi-hued fins, many with opalescent blue spots along the back and sides. What an array of colour indeed.

In the course of a couple of hours we have landed fifty fish ranging from about two to thirty pounds, with an average weight of about six pounds. There is no art in landing these fish; they bite greedily, a sharp pull on the line to drive the hook home and a rapid hauling from the bottom to keep the fish away from the coral with as tight a strain as the line will stand—and in a short time, measured usually in seconds only, the fish is on the deck thumping the boards heavily with its tail as it continues its swimming movement.

It is interesting to see how in the space of an hour or two the merest tiro develops into an experienced angler. Not only can he tell you the species of fish he has on his line long before he sees it, but often he will distinguish between the various kinds by the manner in which they strike his bait. "Ah, another sweetlip," he exclaims, and four times out of five he is wrong, but it savours of the experienced angler and just that far serves its purpose.

Curious that it should happen that way, but the sweet young thing of the party, enjoying her honeymoon in the romantic setting of a coral island, hooked a Queensland groper. Squealing excitedly she calls to hubby to help her— she has hooked a giant shark or a whale or something. Hubby grabs her line and, after a strenuous tussle, his wife dancing round and giving instructions what to do as the fish begins to throw its weight about (instructions which hubby, experienced angler that he is, invariably ignores), the fish is brought to the surface, gaffed, and hauled on board. Then ensues the usual argument over its weight. It is probably fifty pounds, but who would deny the gentle angler's estimate of a hundred pounds? Her's is not alone an angler's prerogative. And so that hundred-pound groper will go down in history as the best fish, the best bit of fishing, of the day. Any one can haul a fish aboard; that's simply a matter of brute strength—it's the hooking of the fish that counts. She said so. Many times. And now that I have related its true history I feel ungallant, ashamed, and sincerely hope our fair angler never reads this book.

Such is a typical day's fishing on the reef. Of course, there are times when very few fish are to be had, but they are the exception rather than the rule, and in many parts of the Barrier the boat rarely returns without a good haul. Winter or summer, day or night, coral fish bite freely.

And now we shall spend a day with the rod fishermen at Hayman Island in the Whitsunday Group.

We are astir before daybreak because the early morning fishing is usually the best. Making for the mess-room we find some of the party already preparing a cup of tea, while others are overhauling their rods, oiling their reels, or attaching their lures, some of feathers, others in the form of automatic strikers. No time is lost over refreshments; a few sandwiches are washed down with a cup or two of tea and the party makes for the beach to the accompaniment of the melodious chatter of currawongs and the boisterous laughter of kookaburras as they greet the dawn in the magnolias and beach oaks fringing the shore.

The day has broken fine and clear but a fresh breeze from the south-east, unusual during July, causes some concern. We pack into a dinghy till there are but three or four inches of freeboard and, although one of the party puts his whole weight behind the oars, we make slow progress against the choppy sea. The dinghy is overcrowded with rods, legs, and cameras. All safely aboard, the engine kicks over in an instant and we head for the channel south of the island for we intend to fish off the eastern shores of Hook Island. But the fish may be anywhere, and this channel has frequently provided great sport, so the lines are dropped overboard. Four anglers make themselves comfortable, their rods secured by a strong harness encircling their backs, their lures trailing from fifteen to thirty yards astern according to the whim of the individual angler. At last the day has arrived that has rarely been out of the anglers' minds for months past—a whole year's work has been done to win this holiday. Surely the guardian deity of all anglers is watching over them; surely he will realize what this day means to his devout disciples.

And so we troll. One hour, two, three hours pass, and not a sign of a fish is seen. This is unusual, but our anglers show no sign of despair—hope springs eternal in their breasts. But why no fish? After the same time on their first day out last year a dozen fish were scattered about the deck. But the tide is on the ebb and the water, churned up by the breeze as it comes from the shallow water inshore, is slightly milky. Perhaps when the tide turns, bringing in the crystal clear water from deeper regions, the fish will be attracted by the lures dancing along the surface in the wash astern.

To those of us who are not fishing time begins to drag; our eyes cease to watch the lures for the swish of the strike and we gaze over the water reflecting from the sun a silvery sheen which scintillates with a myriad points of light. And as we cruise along the coast of Hook Island with its lofty peaks now obscured as a fleecy cloud drifts over them, we find our interest transferred to the grandeur of the scenery about us. Rugged lichen-covered rocks, mottled grey and brown, rise hundreds of feet sheer from the water with here and there a pine-tree apparently growing in the solid rock; now we pass a dense forest of pines with trunks as straight as match sticks, while on the summits of the ridges great walls of rock stand gaunt like the ruined castles of some giants of the past. Here the vegetation is dense but stunted, and an occasional pine-tree towers, sentinel-like, high above it. An osprey's nest, a crude affair of interlaced sticks about six feet in diameter, is perched on the summit of some barren rocks fifty feet or so above the water, the owner peering at us over the top, apparently wondering what we are about.

Engrossed by the beauty about us, our reverie is interrupted by one of the anglers coming forward. He had a

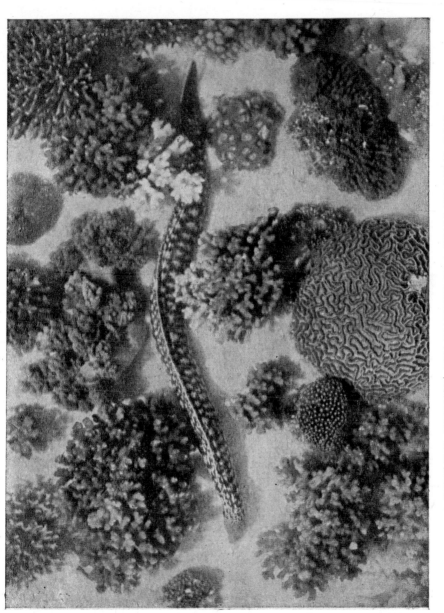

PLATE 40.

A REEF EEL ENJOYING THE WARMTH OF A SHALLOW CORAL POOL

strike and missed, and now he must give way to another until again his turn comes round. Disconsolate, he lies on the deck to ponder over his mistake.

There is a swish astern, a fish flashes momentarily at the surface, a reel screeches, and a Spanish mackerel races away with incredible speed. Far in the distance he leaps high in the air, throws the hook, and bounds away to freedom. Another angler joins us amidships and complains that he allowed too much slack; he is out of touch, but some fish will pay the penalty when he gets his hand in.

And so the morning wears on with a faint promise only of the excitement we had been told was in store for us. Then from out the galley a faint sizzling greets our ears and the smell of fish frying fills our nostrils. The morning on the water has sharpened our appetites, and the sizzling and spluttering below is music in our ears. It seems a long time before that fish is cooked but at last, with palates moist and keen, we accept the invitation shouted from below, "Lunch is ready." A liberal helping of Spanish mackerel caught the afternoon before is devoured with a relish that is but due to a fish of such fine flavour and texture. The mackerel is not only the best sporting fish but is also one of the finest eating fish of the Barrier Reef; though just a trifle dry its flavour and the firmness of its flesh are a real delight.

During lunch there are but two topics of conversation— the excellence of the fish and the cause of the morning's poor sport. Alone amongst us the skipper retains his confidence; he goes so far as to guarantee good sport when the tide turns; moreover, he reminds us that the breeze has dropped. Somehow, we have great faith in our skipper; he has angled over the reef since boyhood and he impresses us that he knows all its peculiarities. And so our anglers, refreshed and inspired with renewed confidence, again take up their stations.

It is about half-past three when the fun begins. We run into a great school of giant mackerel; they appear excited at our coming and leap into the air as if to signal their delight. Wherever we look there appears to be at least one fish out of the water. The anglers stiffen their backs, take a firmer grip of their rods, stare intently at their lures. A flashing green back momentarily breaks the water, a reel screams, and the fight is on, the other anglers winding in their lines to give their more fortunate companion a free field to work in. Instantly the fish strikes, our skipper throws the engine into neutral, ready in a moment to race it forward or astern, to manoeuvre the boat this way or that in order to prevent the fish from making to the front of the boat and so fouling the angler's line. The first mad rush over the fish turns, then plunges down, the angler putting more drag on his reel to prevent the fish sounding too deeply; realizing the futility of its downward flight the fish now makes for the surface; with a great bound it leaps high in the air, hitting the water on its return with a resounding smack, to race away again just beneath the surface at a speed that fills us with amazement. Now it rushes towards the boat and the skipper gives the engine full throttle; no orders are necessary from angler to engine-room; the skipper has manoeuvred his boat in similar circumstances hundreds, thousands of times, and knows what to do in every emergency.

And so this infuriated fish fights every inch for its freedom, with the angler using every resource he knows to keep it where he wants it. Again it goes down; again more drag is put on the reel; over bends the rod at an alarming angle. The angler now begins to pump; throwing his body back he heaves on his rod, then leans forward and winds in the slack. This is hard work and beads of perspiration begin to gather on his forehead. The fish is stubborn but foot by foot it is brought closer to the surface. Is the fight over? As the fish sights the boat it tears away in another mad rush taking about fifty yards of line out. And then the fish, five feet of fighting fury, turns again towards the boat; with a mad rush it leaps clear over the stern and we see its glistening black eye staring at us, we see a row of sharp, vicious teeth as the fish, stiff as a ramrod, cleaves the air above us. As it hits the water it sends a shower of spray over us and when next we sight it, it is thirty or forty yards away.

But it now shows signs of tiring and gradually the angler becomes its master; its rushes are shorter and less speedy; each is nearer the boat than that which preceded it, until at last, every ounce of its fighting strength exhausted, it is brought alongside; a gaff is thrust into it and many willing hands haul it aboard. There it lies, its handsome green back and silvery sides glistening in the sunlight; reviving a little it flings itself about the deck fiercely snapping its pointed jaws. It is a noble fish whose fighting spirit was subdued only when it was exhausted beyond further effort.

And as we admire it our angler takes off his shirt and with a towel wipes the sweat from his body. He is tired, very, but his countenance is aglow. He has had his thrill for the day and is content.

Of course, there is the usual conjecture about the weight of the fish, but no angler's exaggerated estimate is allowed to pass in this company. There are rules governing the strength of the line to be used, the length of the trace, the length of double line connected to the trace, and all records of weights must be accurate, for trophies are allotted for the heaviest fish caught in various classes. This mackerel is found to turn the scale at fifty-three pounds.

But we are still in this school of fish and all four lines are again over the stern while the boat circles about amongst them. In a few minutes a reel begins to spin, followed by another, then another; yes, the fourth goes also. All four lines are tearing away together. Each angler concentrates on his own fish; as one winds his reel to draw the fish nearer the boat another pays his line out as his quarry dashes away in an irresistible rush. Two of them, swimming in opposite directions, cross, and the anglers change places, their right hands on their reels, their eyes on their lines. For fully five minutes the combined fight is on when one of the four finds his line is slack. Thoroughly sorry for himself he reels in and discovers that another fish has bitten his line at the swivel. The three remaining anglers scarcely notice his misfortune; this is no time for sympathy. The skill of the skipper is now tested to the utmost; he must manoeuvre his boat to give each angler a fair chance, and this calls for fine judgment when fish are tearing away in opposite directions. For about a quarter of an hour the fight continues when one of the anglers brings to gaff a mackerel weighing twenty-seven pounds. This leaves more room for the remaining two who, aided by the skilful movements of the launch, manage to manoeuvre their fish out of each other's way. At the end of twenty-five minutes the second fish, weighing thirty-six pounds, is landed, and our sole remaining angler continues the fight against his fish which, judging from the tussle he is having, is the heaviest of them all. Eventually he brings it alongside. It turns the scale at forty-four pounds.

And so the afternoon passes. Before the sun's last rays are fading into twilight fifteen large mackerel can be counted

PLATE 41.

PANDANUS-TREES EXPOSED TO THE WIND, HERON ISLAND

The two dark patches in the water just beyond the ridge of coral rock consist of dense shoals of small fishes known as hardyheads.

strewn about the deck. One might reasonably assume that after such a strenuous afternoon's work (for hard work it certainly was) our angler friends' lust for game would have been completely satiated, but there is no satisfying an angler whose pulse quickens to the run of the reel, and after tea and a consultation with the skipper it is decided to moor the launch in a quiet bay and angle for reef fish.

The night air is balmy but cool and we wrap rugs about ourselves as we lie on the deck above the wheel-house. No longer the thrill of the screeching reel, but quietly and efficiently the anglers haul their catches to the surface, and we have difficulty in determining what species they are as they are freed from the hook by the light of a hurricane lamp. The silence of the night is broken only by the lapping of the water against the boat as she rides at anchor, by an occasional flopping of the fish about the deck, and by the plaintive cries of curlews from the wooded depths of the island, dark and mysterious, towering high above us on our starboard quarter.

Suddenly one of the anglers stumbles as he makes a dash for a heavy line he had left unattended as he fished for smaller fry. Into the night his line is drawn with a strength which his bare fingers cannot check, and, handing the line to the angler nearest him, he hastily dons his gloves to save his fingers from scorching and cutting. No spectacular leaps, no rapid skimming over the surface of the water, just a dead weight as the monster (obviously a shark from its movements) sulks at the end of the line. Now the angler gains a few yards, now he is forced to give way as the shark moves away from the boat. And thus the tussle continues, each opponent momentarily gaining an advantage. At the end of an hour the shark is alongside, subdued but still uncon-

o

quered, and three shots are fired into its brain or at least where its brain is conjectured to be. In the dim light of the lamp it is turned over on its back, its mouth, bordered by a row of vicious triangular teeth, grinning even in death. Shall we haul it on board or cut it adrift? It is left to the angler who caught it to decide, and we find him quite indifferent, for hand-lining does not count in the records of this august band of fishermen, and so the line is cut and we watch the ugly brute sink slowly out of sight.

It was a tiger shark about ten feet in length, and the ocean has been bereft of one of its greatest marauders. Somehow every one felt intense satisfaction at the capture of that shark. One can easily feel sorry for a mackerel or any of the other food fishes as they lie gasping on the deck, but a shark—sly, repulsive, cowardly—who can show the slightest sympathy for its suffering? Yet, after all, there is no blame attaching to it for its apparent misdemeanours towards mankind; if occasionally it attacks us it does so in the ordinary course of its feeding; we are perhaps too apt to attribute it to malice, and in doing so frequently treat the creature with unnecessary harshness.

Again the anglers settle down to their fishing, but the fish have apparently been scared by the presence of the shark and the bites are now few.

Drawing our rugs tightly about us we turn on our backs and gaze up into the heavens. The night is dark but clear, and the stars above appear far more numerous than in the southern regions whence we come. The lap of the water against the boat is very soothing; the curlews appear to be retreating farther and farther into the island, the sounds of voices grow dimmer and more confused till at last they die completely away.

SOME GAME FISH OF THE BARRIER

The Spanish mackerel is the principal sporting fish of the Great Barrier Reef. The largest specimen recorded is said to have weighed a hundred and twenty-one pounds; it was caught by a professional fisherman. The largest caught by an amateur with rod and reel, using thirty-six-thread line, weighed sixty-eight and a half pounds, and on fifteen-thread line, sixty-pounds. Although it may be taken along the edges of the tide rips of the outer barrier during the whole of the year, it is during the months from May to October that anglers seek it amongst the islands between the outer barrier and the mainland. During May and June it is found in greatest abundance in the southern end of the reef about the islands of the Bunker and Capricorn groups; it then works north and about the middle or the end of June makes its appearance in the Whitsunday Group where it is usually captured in great numbers till September or October. The average run of mackerel weigh from twenty-five to thirty-five pounds. It is usual to fish for them with either eighteen- or fifteen-thread lines of the finest quality cuttyhunk, though some experienced anglers frequently use nine-thread lines.

Even surpassing the mackerel in fighting qualities, but unfortunately far less common, the queenfish, shaped like the mackerel but more closely allied to the kingfish and trevally, is caught in a similar manner and in similar situations, and, although it grows only to a weight of about thirty pounds, weight for weight it is probably one of the most spectacular, tenacious, and active fighters amongst the game fishes of the world. It leaps into the air with great frequency and occasionally dances along the surface with its tail only in the water; indeed, it has been stated by experienced anglers that a queenfish weighing twenty pounds will put up as good a fight and pull as hard as a mackerel of twice that weight.

The most stubborn fighter of the reef is probably the turrum, a giant trevally which attains a weight of upwards of seventy pounds; the largest landed by an amateur on rod and reel with regulation tackle weighing seventy-two pounds. The average size, however, probably ranges between twenty and thirty pounds. The turrum is not so spectacular as the mackerel or queenfish, but is more tenacious and more stubborn; it does not waste its energy in frantic leaps but usually sounds and fights deeply, and when a large turrum is hooked its capture tries the patience of the most ardent angler, for it tires very slowly. When alive it is an object of great beauty, its iridescent silvery sides flashing like a brilliant sunset.

Another important game fish of the reef is the giant pike, a pugnacious fish with long, needle-like teeth greatly feared by naked divers upon whom it has been known to make vicious attacks, tearing great pieces of flesh from their bodies. This fish averages from thirty to forty pounds with a length of about four feet six inches, the largest recorded on rod and reel weighing fifty-one pounds. The giant pike is closely related to the American barracuda. Both the turrum and the pike are frequently hooked when fishing at the bottom.

Other important game fish of the reef, which occasionally provide great sport, are the tunny, little tunny, kingfish, albacore, and bonito, while swordfish (marlins) are sometimes landed and are probably more common than is at present realized. The deeper water beyond the outer barrier has yet to be fished for them.

The angler proceeding to the Barrier Reef is advised to equip himself with 100 yards of No. 10 gut, 100 yards of No. 5 gut, and 100 yards of heavy cord line, and 3/0, 5/0,

PLATE 42.

ANGLING FOR SPANISH MACKEREL AND OTHER GAME FISH
OFF HOOK ISLAND
Photo: T. C. Roughley.

SPANISH MACKEREL WEIGHING 68 POUNDS
Photo: J. McKim.

PLATE 43.

PACKING PEARL SHELL AT THURSDAY ISLAND FOR EXPORT
Photo: Capt. Frank Hurley.

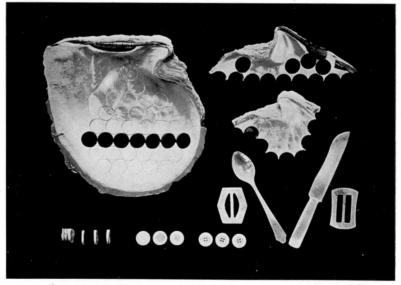

THE MANUFACTURE OF PEARL BUTTONS AND FANCY GOODS FROM
PEARL SHELL
Photo: T. C. Roughley.

and 7/0 hooks for reef fishing. If intent on trolling with
a rod he should provide himself with a sturdy reel capable
of holding 300 to 400 yards of fifteen-thread line (cuttyhunk). Swivels of sizes 1/0 to 4/0 may be used; they
should be darkened, for game fish are attracted by bright
swivels and are apt to cut the line in their vicinity. Wire
traces of best quality game-fish wire should be at least five
feet long. Hooks of sizes 8/0, 9/0, and 12/0, extra strong,
and lures such as Knowles automatic strikers of sizes Nos
6 and 7, feathered lures of sizes Nos 9 and 10, and lightning
spinners of size No. 4, are all necessary parts of the equipment. The use of a rod-rest and harness when trolling is
permissible according to the rules of the angling clubs.

CHAPTER SIXTEEN

Sea Birds Gather in Millions

THE wonders of the Great Barrier Reef are interminable; nor is its interest confined to the wealth beneath its waters, for the birds that congregate there vie with the marine life to stimulate our interest and excite our wonder. All contrive to lend the reef a fascination that is surely unrivalled by any similar area in the world.

If in the summer-time you sail over the blue waters of the Barrier Reef it is not unlikely that from the distance a coral island will appear as if surmounted by a black cloud, while from its direction a peculiar faint murmuring reaches your ears. Gradually, as you approach more closely, the dark cloud resolves itself first into a mass of moving specks, then into an enormous number of birds wheeling and turning as they flutter over the tree-tops, and the murmuring increases to a raucous, screeching din. You have arrived at an island where terns are breeding, and if you pause awhile you will find much to interest you. The terns you have seen are probably sooty or wide-awake terns, which are the most active of the many species inhabiting the reef. You may land on another island without seeing a bird as you approach it, but the trees are full of their nests, and half the population is scattered over the water procuring food for those whose domestic duties demand their presence at home. During the day all is quiet, but at night when the birds return from their foraging there are mates and young to be fed, quarrels to be settled, domestic entanglements to be straightened out, and pandemonium reigns till dawn.

Many were the tales told in the early days by superstitious mariners of the weird and awesome noises emanating from some of the islands of the reef at night; they appeared to be haunted by a legion of lost souls moaning and wailing as in an inferno. These sounds heard afar off came from a choir of perhaps a million voices as the mutton-birds and noddy terns made love in their own peculiar way.

During the colder months of the year these birds are widely distributed over the Pacific Ocean, but spring calls them to the islands of the Barrier Reef for mating and nesting purposes. Their numbers are enormous. At North-West Island in the Capricorn Group, which is only about two and a half miles in circumference and comprises an area of about three hundred acres, mutton-birds quartered there during the breeding-season have been estimated by various authorities to number between one and two millions, while the population of the noddy terns nesting at the same time has been estimated at about half that number. Now, these are not small birds; the mutton-bird is about the size of a small duck and the noddy tern about the size of a pigeon; it can readily be imagined, therefore, that the mutton-birds, which burrow in the soft sandy soil, occupy almost every square foot of the island, and the noddies, whose nests are built in trees, make use of every available branch.

The mutton-bird, also known as the wedge-tailed shear-water from its habit of skimming close to the surface of the water during its flight, and also as the wedge-tailed petrel, grows to a length of about sixteen inches; it is a dark chocolate brown with a wedge-shaped tail and a reddish bill which is strongly hooked. The smaller noddy tern, or white-capped noddy as it is frequently termed, grows to a length of about thirteen or fourteen inches; its plumage is dark grey, almost black, and the crown of its head is white or greyish-white.

Both the mutton-bird and the white-capped noddy breed on the larger coral islands of the reef. The Capricorn and Bunker groups are favourite nesting-places, and in the breeding-season they are to be found in great numbers on North-West, Tryon, Heron, and Masthead islands in the Capricorns, and on Lady Musgrave, Hoskyn, and Fairfax islands in the Bunkers.

In view of the vast numbers of both birds that flock to the islands at night one would expect that the mingling of them would lead to the greatest rivalry and confusion; on the contrary their interests rarely clash for, as if by mutual arrangement, they work to different time-tables. In September they begin to gather on the islands. The terns, after the day's foraging for fish and other marine life at the surface, arrive at the island and settle on the trees before sunset, then the mutton-birds, skimming gracefully over the surface of the water like giant swallows, touching it with the tip of one wing then the other, assemble over the reef flat surrounding the island till the air is full of them, and as darkness approaches they fly over the tall Pisonia-trees in increasing numbers as they endeavour to locate a likely spot to land or perhaps to determine the site of last year's mateship. One after another they flop down, hitting the soft sand with a dull thud, and if returning to the island for the first time since their sojourn there of the previous season, begin to search round for last year's burrow, but if they are returning from a day's foraging over the waters they alight unerringly almost at its entrance. Their sense of location and direction is uncanny.

Soon after alighting the birds begin their courting. It is usual for each male to seek last year's mate and if located all is well, but sometimes his mate does not appear, and there are many widows whose husbands have been lost in the intervening period. And, of course, there are last year's fledgelings which have to find a mate. The rivalry is tremendously keen. A male, anxiously wandering about the island and espying a female without an escort, moves towards her with wings half spread, and crouching down with head and neck extended he utters a plaintive, pleading murmur. Watching her intently he advances slowly, his note increases in volume and frequency till it is a loud wailing or crooning, and at last, if his advances are accepted, he sidles up to her and they caress each other affectionately with their bills, stroke each other's head and neck and —purr like contented cats.

But perhaps a rival appears on the scene. Each strives to outdo the other in ostentation; each tries to drown the other's voice. If the lady's fancy falls on one, the other makes off, crest-fallen, disconsolate. Possibly the lady is not impressed by either of them and waddling away leaves them to commiserate with each other's misfortune. At times considerable numbers, perhaps thirty or forty, of both sexes will gather in the clearings that are devoid of vegetation; the rivalry then becomes terrific and the noise a babel of many strange tongues. One by one they pair off and move away and, their love consummated, they begin house-hunting if they have not already waiting for them the home of last year's courtship. If a new home must be constructed the female, sometimes assisted by the male, begins to dig vigorously; scratching alternately with each leg an almost continuous spray of sand is thrown backwards as the tunnel is dug at an angle with the surface; but even if last year's burrow awaits them a thorough spring-cleaning is necessary, for much sand has fallen from the walls, and leaves and other debris are littered about the interior. What a hive of industry this island is for a month or more after the first of the birds make their appearance!

And what a din arises from the island as thousands upon thousands of the birds make love. From their first arrival at dusk right throughout the night the air is rent by a continuous moaning, groaning, and caterwauling, while out of the darkness above some belated arrival passes overhead wailing, perhaps lest his loved one, impatient at his delay, has fallen for the wiles of another. Added to this is the chattering and croaking of the noddies busy with their own love-making in the branches of the trees above, and for complete variety the shrill clarion of feral roosters intermittently rises above the incessant din.

At about three o'clock in the morning a move is made for the day's fishing ahead. Radiating in all directions from the interior of the island tracks lead to larger tracks which join up with broader avenues, until finally a pathway which may be up to six feet in width leads to an elevation at the top of the beach. There may be upwards of twenty main pathways for the exit of the birds on the one island, and from them the smaller tracks ramify inwards like the branches of a tree. It has been computed that as many as five hundred birds may pass each minute along one of the main arteries. At about three o'clock, then, some of the earliest are astir, making their way to the exits; for a while they straggle along, then in twos and threes, till by half-past three they pass along in an almost continuous stream, on the larger tracks perhaps eight or ten abreast, jostling, hurrying like a crowd of factory workers anxious to sign on before the whistle blows. Much love-making is in progress during the procession and the noisy clamour continues to disturb the night air. Perhaps two quarrel and fight, holding up the procession to the discomfiture of the impatient mob behind them. At the sides may be several males, unsuccessful in their approaches of the previous evening; they croon and wail in an endeavour to attract some unattached female; frequently fortune favours them, and belatedly, they make amends for the lack of companionship of the night before.

Leave-taking over, the birds run a short distance down the slope, take wing, and fly far off over the waters in quest of the fishes, the squid, and other forms of marine life that constitute their food.

The first gleam of daylight finds all the mutton-birds scattered about the surface of the ocean, or at least all except those whose duties at home demand their presence on the nest. It is then that the noddies, awakened by the peeping of the sun over the horizon (that is, if they have slept at all through the din), rise from their nests in the trees and, after hovering over the reef for a short time, fly away to sea. The noddies, then, are first to bed and last to rise.

After a few weeks an increasing number of burrows will be found to contain eggs. One egg only is laid, and it is cared for by both parents; sometimes the female will remain in the burrow all day, its food being brought home at night by the male, or the male will take his turn at incubating. As the summer advances more and more young ones will be found sharing the burrows with their parents; these remain under parental care and are fed nightly till the following autumn (April to June) when their down has been replaced by feathers and they are able to fend for themselves. As the development of their plumage nears completion they leave the burrows during the course of several nights to exercise their wings, but should they enter the water while much down still remains, their impetuosity usually results in their death from drowning.

By the end of June all the birds, both adults and young, have left the island to roam wide over the Pacific till the desire for procreation again seizes them. But their burrows remain. May I suggest that you walk through the island and experience them for yourself. As you walk you will find a leg sinking to the knee as it breaks through the shallow roof, filling your shoe with sand. The whole island is honeycombed with them and they frequently make progress difficult. Sinking into a burrow is usually considered great fun, but there are times when it may become somewhat exasperating. Such an experience befell me one day on Heron Island when I was endeavouring to obtain a photograph of some Pisonia-trees with a stand camera on a tripod. It seemed almost impossible to locate a spot where one of the legs of the tripod would not sink deeply into a mutton-bird's burrow, and when at last I had all three legs stable I moved back a step as, with my head beneath the dark cloth, I began to focus, and the sand giving way beneath me, down I sprawled on the broad of my back dragging the camera on top of me. At the moment I wished to goodness these birds nested in trees, but after reflection I came to the conclusion that even that would be likely to have its disadvantages.

THE COURTING OF THE NODDY TERN

While the courting of the mutton-birds is proceeding on the ground the white-capped noddies are just as intent on their own love-affairs in the trees above. In the Pisonias, in the fig-trees where they occur, and to a less extent in the Pandanus-trees and Tournefortias, noddies are busy courting, mating, nest-building, incubating, or feeding their newly-hatched young.

PLATE 44.

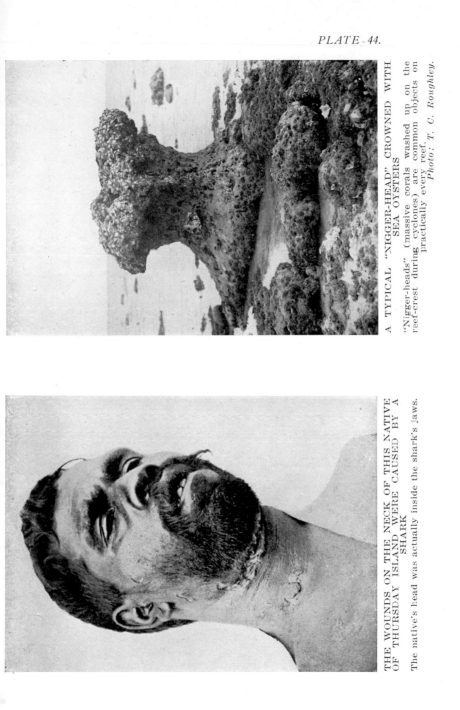

A TYPICAL "NIGGER-HEAD" CROWNED WITH SEA OYSTERS

"Nigger-heads" (massive corals washed up on the reef-crest during cyclones) are common objects on practically every reef.

Photo: T. C. Roughley.

THE WOUNDS ON THE NECK OF THIS NATIVE OF THURSDAY ISLAND WERE CAUSED BY A SHARK

The native's head was actually inside the shark's jaws.

The trees are full of them. As many as a hundred and forty-three nests occupied by them have been counted in one Pisonia-tree; with two birds to each nest and some recently hatched young the total was brought up to over three hundred birds inhabiting the one tree. And this was typical of many others.

The courtship of the noddy is a delight to watch, for it is performed with a delicacy and finesse shared by few other birds. Amongst his tribe he is the perfect lover. Moving along a branch towards a female of his choice, he sidles close to her, then bows and nods his head, the while sounding a note like a frog or perhaps the stridulating of a cricket. Approvingly the female returns his bow and nod, and then begins as choice an example of caressing as could be imagined; he strokes her head and neck with his beak, and beak to beak they cuddle together, each alternately crooning the same love-song. At length, satisfied that he is the chosen one, the male opens wide his mouth, regurgitates the fish he has stored in his crop, and invites his lady-love to dinner. She seems immensely pleased.

When mating is completed the task of nest-building begins. A careful survey of likely spots is made, both birds chattering the while, and when an agreement is reached they fly to the ground to gather the pliable yellow leaves of the Pisonia-tree; very fresh or very dry leaves are of little use, for they are not amenable to manipulation into the shape required. A few of the right type are carried to the branch and pressed down with the feet and arranged with the beak. Portions of seaweed are gathered from the beach, and some green grass from above it, and these are used to consolidate the considerable quantity of Pisonia leaves that must be requisitioned before the nest is completed; finally the excrement of the birds themselves serves as a binding material and gives the whole a white-washed appearance. The nest when completed is about five or six inches across the upper surface and several inches thick; in the centre is a depression just deep enough to prevent the egg falling off.

The nest may be built anywhere on the tree from a height of three to fifty feet, though the position most favoured is from fifteen to twenty feet from the ground, where the birds obtain the greatest amount of shade and shelter.

During nest-building both birds are extremely industrious; competition is keen for leaves of the required degree of pliability, and much thieving goes on. It is quite common to see a neighbour fly stealthily to the nest of another and pick off a leaf that has just been arranged with much care by the owner who has momentarily left to search for more.

Frequently the cementing of the noddy's nest is aided by the seed-heads of the Pisonia-tree, which are extremely sticky, but the gathering of them is attended with considerable risk, for they are liable to stick to the feathers and render flight impossible; in this condition the bird cannot leave the ground, and as it struggles it gathers more and more of them; sticks and leaves adhere to the viscid secretion, and the bird is rendered so helpless that it eventually perishes.

A considerable mortality occurs during every breeding-season from this cause; the seeds stick at the slightest touch, and their removal is very difficult. The Torres Strait pigeons also suffer many casualties from the same agency.

One egg only is laid; it may be pure white, spotted, or blotched. Both birds take turns at incubating, and the male continues to display the same affection and solicitude towards the female as during his period of courtship. He will perch close to her, and when he considers that she has done her fair share of sitting, he gently and politely nudges her and she moves quietly off to allow him to take her place. The bird that is off nesting duty flies away to procure food for its mate.

By the beginning of December many young have hatched out. The newly-hatched bird with its black body and white crown is a delightful ball of fluff—and petulant, too; if molested it pecks with its little bill quite viciously, and if it has been fed it is likely to disgorge its food.

What a tremendous amount of food is required to feed these great colonies of nesting birds! Whence is it obtained? The surface waters of the Barrier Reef are extremely prolific in small fishes and squid, and heavy toll is taken of them during each nesting-period. Round many of the islands small fishes known as "hardyheads," which grow to a length of about four inches, frequently congregate in shoals so dense that they lie like a solid mass in the water; they appear to offer themselves as a sacrifice to the terns, the mutton-birds, and a host of others which forgather on the islands during the summer months.

In addition to the toll taken by the seeds of the Pisonia-tree, the sea-eagles, of which almost every island appears to have at least one pair with a nest perched in the highest of the trees, reap a rich harvest both of terns and mutton-birds, while on several of the islands domestic cats gone wild prey upon them extensively.

OTHER TERNS

Although the white-capped noddy is the commonest of the terns in the southern area of the reef, there are several other species that occur there in considerable numbers, while in the more northerly region it may be greatly outnumbered by other species.

It is customary for each species to choose a particular

island for nesting-purposes and to return to it each year. A great clashing of interests is thereby avoided. Occasionally, however, two species may live together in perfect harmony, and an instance of this is to be seen on Wilson Island, one of the Capricorns, where the roseate tern and the black-naped tern nest on the same shingle beach, the former occupying the higher part of the beach near the fringing vegetation, and the latter the lower part nearer high-tide mark. The roseate tern deposits her eggs, usually two in number, amongst small shrubs, in creepers, or near large stones where there is a certain amount of shelter from the sun, and the black-naped tern gathers coral pebbles and fragments of sea-shells, which are arranged between stones to form a receptacle for the eggs.

Crested terns nest in large colonies on Masthead Island in the Capricorns; the eggs are laid on the sand or grass, and no attempt whatever is made to construct a nest.

Farther north great colonies of wide-awake or sooty terns inhabit numbers of the islands. On Michaelmas Cay, northeast of Cairns, the eggs of the wide-awakes may be so numerous during the breeding-season from October to January, lying on the bare sand or amongst the grass, that it is difficult to walk about the island without treading on them, and when the birds are on the wing they congregate in such dense flocks overhead that the sky is almost obscured, while their continuous screeching is positively deafening. This restless tern is on the wing most of the day and frequently during much of the night.

THE TORRES STRAIT PIGEON

Another bird that visits the islands between the Barrier and the mainland in great numbers during the summer months is the Torres Strait pigeon, also called the nutmeg pigeon because of its partiality for the fruit of the wild nut-

PLATE 45.

FRUIT OF THE PANDANUS-TREE OR "SCREW-PINE"
(One-third natural size.)

meg. What a tragic history this handsome, snowy-white bird has had! Before the advent of white man the aborigines took toll of great numbers; climbing trees where the birds were alighting they killed many with long sticks or perhaps threw nulla-nullas into the densely-crowded homing flocks, and carried loads of them back to the mainland in their canoes. In spite of this havoc the coming of white man found the pigeons in enormous numbers, but owing to the ruthless slaughter of the nesting birds by so-called sportsmen their numbers have been decimated till now thousands only are seen where their numbers could formerly be measured in hundreds of thousands. The slaughter by the aborigines can be excused; amongst a people who knew not even the rudiments of tilling the soil, whose weapons were of the most primitive type, flocks of birds to be obtained so easily came to them like manna from heaven; but they killed for food, for their very sustenance. What can be said of the slaying by white people? Perhaps the less the better; but indignation cannot help being felt at the thought of such ruthless, such senseless, slaughter, for much of this wholesale shooting was indulged in out of a perverted sense of "sport"—or rather, should we say, a primitive lust to kill? But let us draw a veil over this sorry picture. The bird is now protected, and we can only hope that its numbers increase to something like their former dimensions.

The Torres Strait pigeon comes south from New Guinea and the islands of Torres Strait during August and September to nest on the islands, principally those close to the mainland, within the Great Barrier Reef. Its appearance off the eastern Queensland coast corresponds fairly closely with the ripening of the wild nutmeg, and the development of that fruit was watched by the aborigines, as we would now watch a calendar, in expectation of its arrival. On reaching the

P

island of its choice, pairing takes place, and a rude nest is constructed by arranging twigs in the fork made by two horizontal branches of a tree. Many different trees, such as tea-trees, palms, and a variety of shrubs, are used for nesting-purposes, but the most favoured are the mangroves.

At dawn the birds fly low over the water to the mainland where they scatter in search of the native fruits and berries, such as quandongs, native plums, and their beloved nutmegs, which they carry back to the island in their crops just before sunset. We shall listen to Banfield (now an old friend) describe for us their return from the mainland:

"Towards the end of the breeding-season, when the multitude has almost doubled its strength by lusty young recruits, for an hour and more before sunset until a few minutes after, there is a never-ending procession from the mainland to the favoured islands—a great, almost uncountable host. Soon some of the tree-tops are swaying under the weight of the masses of white birds. The whirr and rush of flight, the clacking and slapping of wings, the domineering "coo-hoo-oo" of the male birds and the responsive notes of the hens, the tumult when in alarm all take wing simultaneously and wheel and circle and settle again with rustling and creaking branches, the sudden swoop with whistling wings of single birds close overhead—all this creates a perpetual din. Then, as darkness follows hard upon the sinking of the sun, the birds hustle among the thick foliage of the jungle, with querulous, inquiring notes and much ado. Gradually the sounds subside, and the subdued monotonous rhythm of the sea alone is heard."

Banfield wrote this prior to 1908 when already the numbers of the birds had been greatly reduced, but, although he lamented the slaughter that had thinned their ranks even then, the great flocks he saw and described are no more. The "great, almost uncountable host" can now easily be numbered.

On arrival at the island after the day's gathering of food, the bird regurgitates the hard nuts, which litter the bases of the trees, and the fruity, outer covering or mace is fed to the nesting mate and young.

By the end of March the young birds are strong enough on the wing to withstand the great journey north, and then the flocks depart to scatter over the islands of Torres Strait and the mainland of New Guinea, till the following spring, when the urge for mating again impels them to make the long journey south.

THE SCRUB FOWL

One of the most interesting of the birds to be found on the mainland islands within the Barrier Reef is the scrub or jungle fowl, which belongs to a small group of birds whose nesting habits are unique. The incubation of the eggs of all the birds we have so far discussed is accomplished by the continued application of the body of one of the parents to provide the regular warmth necessary for incubation and subsequent hatching, but in the case of the scrub fowl this object is attained in an entirely different manner. The parent buries the eggs in great mounds of decaying leaves and other debris where they are left till the young hatch out. This, of course, obviates the monotony of sitting on the eggs for a long period, but it involves a great amount of pre-liminary labour.

For some weeks before the eggs are due to be laid the parents rake up the surface leaves, sand, grass, and small sticks till eventually they assume the form of a great mound. At times several pairs may assist in the work, and it is not uncommon to find the original mound added to year after year, generation after generation, till it reaches enormous proportions. Mounds have been recorded on some of the islands within the Barrier that rise to a height of fifteen feet and are upwards of fifty feet in circumference, the material of which they are composed weighing many tons. One mound on Hook Island, in the Whitsunday Group, has been estimated to contain two hundred tons of sand, leaves, and debris scraped up by many generations of birds.

On completion of the mound the female scoops a hole in its surface to a depth which may vary from about two to six feet, and she then arranges her eggs at the bottom; they are placed upright with the broad end uppermost and a space between them, and the cavity is carefully filled in. The normal clutch probably varies from six to eight eggs, but in the larger mounds, which serve for the incubation of the clutches of several birds, as many as forty or fifty eggs may be found. For a bird somewhat smaller in size than a domestic fowl the eggs are particularly large; they are nearly three times the size of fowls' eggs.

The requisite heat is apparently engendered by the decaying vegetation, which must be in a moist condition for the purpose, and the mounds are therefore always found in a densely-shaded part of the forest where desiccation is reduced to a minimum. The dampness probably serves another purpose, that of altering the consistency of the shell, rendering it more friable to allow of the subsequent escape of the chick.

When the young hatch out they are fully feathered; they at once proceed to scratch their way to the surface through the loosely-heaped debris, and after a short pause hop away to forage for themselves, or they may even fly to the nearest tree. Many probably never see their parents.

PLATE 46.

A FOREST OF PISONIA-TREES

The scrub fowl is an omnivorous feeder, mixing insects, centipedes, and spiders with berries, fruits, and seeds, which it obtains by an incessant raking and scratching of the leaves covering the surface of the ground. Unfortunately it is a good table bird, and its eggs are esteemed as food, consequently great numbers have been destroyed by shooting parties from the mainland, but it is still fairly plentiful on several of the larger islands. The scrub fowl should be rigidly protected for all time, for it is one of the world's wonder birds.

SILVER GULLS

On every island silver gulls are seen flying over or resting on the water. This handsome bird feeds on small fish and is an effective scavenger along the shore-line. It is also a notorious robber of the eggs of other birds, and when the terns are nesting gulls are repeatedly seen to swoop down and steal the egg from some unguarded nest. Its own nest is built usually in grass under shrubs in the outer zone of the island vegetation. The breeding-season extends from October to January and the eggs vary from two to three in number, although as many as five may occasionally be found.

REEF HERONS

Reef herons are also common on most of the islands; when the tide is out they are usually seen wading over the reef searching for the various forms of marine life on which they feed, and when the reef is covered at high tide they congregate on the beaches and rocks. Their nests, consisting of platforms of sticks, may be found on low bushes in well-concealed and well-sheltered situations from September to January, and occasionally throughout the whole of the year. Two, three, and sometimes four eggs are laid.

SEA EAGLES

White-breasted sea eagles, as previously noted, are found on nearly all the islands of the reef, their great nests being perched usually thirty or forty feet up the highest of the trees. They are the terrors of all the smaller birds, and play great havoc with the terns and mutton-birds, while they also include in their diet sea-snakes and many species of fish, a favourite being the skipper, or long-tom, which is doubtlessly seized as it skips over the surface of the water to escape the attack of some predatory foe beneath. On One Tree Island in the Capricorn Group there is a large nest about eight feet above the ground in a clump of Pandanus-trees that was noted by Jukes in the course of his voyage along the reef as long ago as 1844; it is now eight feet long and six feet wide. The breeding-season extends from about June to October and usually two eggs are laid.

The turnstone cannot fail to attract our attention; as it feeds along the water's edge it thrusts its beak under small coral boulders, and with an upward jerk of its head turns the stones over to grab some unlucky morsel lurking beneath them.

FRIGATE-BIRDS AND DOMESTIC FOWLS

Occasionally, soaring high overhead, frigate-birds are to be seen resting on the wind; for hours they remain suspended with scarcely a flutter of the wings. Thus they remain till they espy some luckless birds returning with their day's spoil, when they swoop down at great speed and compel them out of sheer fright to disgorge the contents of their crops, which they seize as it falls towards the water.

Finally, mention must be made of the domestic fowls that many years ago were liberated on some of the Barrier Reef islands. Their plumage has reverted to the black-breasted game type of their ancestors of the Indian jungle, and they appear to thrive on islands where there is no fresh water. Their eggs are laid either on the ground or in depressions formed by the low branches of Pisonia-trees. At Heron Island the eggs are gathered to augment the supply brought from the mainland, though doubtless many are overlooked in the thick scrub. These fowls do no harm at all, but the domestic cats gone wild are a continual pest to bird life and serious efforts should be made to exterminate them.

PEARLS AND PEARL-SHELLS

THE lure of the lustrous pearl urged men into dim and dangerous waters for long ages before the Christian era, for this queen of gems held pride of place in women's eyes (and men's, too, very frequently) from very ancient times. In India, in Persia, in Arabia, pearls were cherished and worn as ornaments by the ladies of the land long before their existence was known to the peoples of western Europe, and when eventually trade developed with those countries pearls became a regular form of barter.

Many and varied were the views held by these ancient people concerning their origin. But the consensus of well-informed opinion was that they developed from drops of dew, and Pliny the elder, in the first century of the Christian era, described their formation in intimate detail in the following words:

"When the genial season of the year exercises its influence on the animal, it is said that, yawning, as it were, it opens its shell, and so receives a kind of dew, by means of which it becomes impregnated; and that at length it gives birth, after many struggles, to the burden of its shell, in the shape of pearls, which vary according to the quality of the dew. If this has been in a perfectly pure state when it flowed into the shell, then the pearl produced is white and brilliant, but if it was turbid, then the pearl is of a clouded colour also; if the sky should happen to have been lowering when it was generated, the pearl will be of a pallid colour; from all which it is quite evident that the quality of the pearl depends much more upon a calm state of the heavens than of the sea, and hence it is that it contracts a cloudy hue, or a limpid appearance, according to the degree of the serenity of the sky in the morning.

"The fish, as soon as ever it perceives the hand, shuts its shell and covers up its treasures, being well aware that it is for them that it is sought; and if it happens to catch the hand, it cuts it off with the sharp edge of the shell. And no punishment is there that could be more justly inflicted. . . . And yet, for all this, the women will not banish these gems from their ears! Some writers say, that these animals live in communities, just like swarms of bees, each of them being governed by one remarkable for its size and its venerable old age; while at the same time it is possessed of marvellous skill in taking all due precautions against danger; the divers, they say, take especial care to find these, and when once they are taken, the others stray to and fro, and are easily caught in their nets."

Grotesque as Pliny's account may seem to us in these enlightened days, it will probably surprise the reader to know that the theory of the dewy origin of pearls prevailed throughout Europe for over fifteen hundred years; indeed, it was not till late in the sixteenth century that it was shown how impossible such an origin was, and even then for a long time afterwards credence was given to it by a great majority of civilized people.

The origin of pearls we now know to be due to the introduction of some foreign substance within the shell of the oyster, either a grain of sand or some similar material, or perhaps a small parasite such as a worm. This foreign substance sets up an irritation of the tissues of the animal; it is consequently isolated by a secretion of mother-of-pearl, and having coated it the animal continues the secretion in a series of concentric layers as long as it lives, the older oysters therefore producing larger pearls than the younger ones. This secretion is not a specialized substance reserved by the animal for the purpose; it is of the same nature as the shell itself, which has a similar but usually less brilliant lustre. This lustre is caused by the minutely wavy surface which consists of myriads of microscopic prisms; the light falling on these at different angles is split up into the many colours that compose it, giving the shell a subdued iridescence.

The shell is secreted from the surface of the animal and by its mantle, and pearls may be found actually within the mantle or attached to the shell. In the latter case they are known as "blister" pearls and are usually of irregular shape. The lustre of the pearl is generally finer than that of the shell itself, due to its greater curvature and frequently also to the finer waves or corrugations on its surface.

Some extremely valuable pearls have been found in Australian pearl-oysters, but on the whole their lustre is more subdued and the pearls themselves more irregular than those from India or Persia. Probably the most renowned was that known as the "Southern Cross" which was found on 26 March 1883, off the coast of Western Australia; it formed a cluster of nine pearls in the design of a Roman cross, about one and a half inches in length. This striking and unusual formation was exhibited at the Indian Exhibition in London in 1886, and later at the Paris Exhibition in 1889, where it created great interest and was awarded a gold medal. The owner valued it at £10,000, but there is no record of the price he received for it, and much speculation has taken place since as to whether the original formation (whatever it was) was not artificially added to in order to form the design of a cross.

Probably the most valuable pearl ever produced from Australian waters was "The Star of the West," a drop-shaped gem about the size of a sparrow's egg and weighing one hundred grains. It was found in 1917 in a shell from the beds of Western Australia, and was valued at £14,000.

At one time the pearls produced by the industry formed an asset of considerable value to the owners of the boats that fished for them, but smuggling by the crews was so rife, and such a constant source of irritation, that eventually the owners decided to allow the Japanese skippers to retain all that were found. Accurate returns of these were not made and consequently it is impossible to estimate their value. The recorded value of the pearls from the whole of Australian waters, from 1927 to 1932 inclusive, averaged £16,625 per annum, but the actual production was probably nearer twice that figure. Recently, however, the terms of employment of the divers were altered materially, and all pearls must now be handed to the owners of the vessels.

The Australian industry, however, is carried on essentially for the shells and not for the pearls they might contain. In this it differs radically from the industry centred round Ceylon, where the shells are small and valueless, but the pearls they contain much more prevalent.

The pearl-shell is the Great Barrier Reef's richest treasure. It occurs in commercial quantities from near the New Guinea coast to about as far south as Cairns, beyond which it becomes increasingly smaller and less abundant, and it is widely distributed amongst and between the coral reefs throughout the length and breadth of Torres Strait. The area of production on the Australian coast is the greatest pearl-shell ground in the world, for it extends over about three thousand miles from east of Torres Strait to south of Broome in Western Australia. These grounds produce about eighty-five per cent of the world's pearl-shell, the rich mother-of-pearl of which it is composed being an important article of commerce for conversion into buttons, sleeve-links, knife-handles, trinkets, and a variety of similar goods. For over sixty years it has formed an important and valuable Australian primary industry.

Not only are the pearling-grounds the most extensive in the world, but the shell is easily the largest of all pearl-shells. Actually there are two species in the Great Barrier Reef area, the silver- or golden-lip and the black-lip. Of these the silver-lip is by far the more valuable, although the black-lip produces the more pearls. The silver-lip may grow to a diameter of about twelve inches with a weight of fourteen pounds; compared with this the black-lip is small and light; it rarely grows beyond a diameter of seven inches and a weight of a pound and a half, though a much greater size is sometimes attained in the South Sea islands, and a pair of shells from the Solomons has been known to reach a diameter of eleven inches.

Now, although this shellfish is usually referred to as a pearl "oyster," it is not a true oyster at all, but is more closely related to the mussel; its flesh is rank in flavour and consequently is rarely if ever eaten. When young it is attached to rocks by means of a thread-like bunch of fibres, but as it grows older these degenerate and larger specimens are found free on the bottom or partially sunk in the sand. They are most numerous in the channels between reefs where the current runs strongly.

Attention appears to have been first directed to the occurrence of pearl-shells in Australian waters by an American sailor named Tays, who in 1861 reported extensive beds on

PLATE 47.

CORAL COD
This fine edible fish grows to a weight of about forty pounds.

KING SNAPPER
This fish is sometimes known as "Government Bream" on account of
the bands crossing its body in the form of a broad arrow.

the north-western coast, but his discovery was not exploited till seven years later when Captain Banner made history by sailing his brig the *Julia Percy* out of Sydney for the pearling-grounds in Torres Strait; he made for the beds adjacent to Warrior Reefs, and so laid the foundation of a new and lucrative industry.

In those days the shells were gathered by searching over the reefs at low tide, but in the course of a few years it became necessary to wade for the better class shells; in a short time this area also was thinned out and then naked diving into the shallow water adjacent to the reefs was resorted to. Gradually the divers were forced deeper and deeper till they had reached the limits of their capabilities, which range to a maximum depth of forty or fifty feet. Having collected the bulk of the shell in this comparatively shallow water the diving-dress was introduced in 1874 to enable the rich grounds offshore to be worked.

Initially the boats, which consisted mostly of schooners, sailed to the grounds from Sydney or Brisbane and returned to those ports with their valuable cargoes; valuable indeed were they then, for the shell brought from £300 to £400 per ton. What fortunes were made in the early days of the fishery! The virgin fields proved to be veritable gold-mines, for not only was the shell very valuable but it was gathered in great quantities in a very short time. On a rich patch the vessel would fill her holds in a few weeks with shells weighing up to ten or twelve pounds each, and one schooner is reported to have collected two tons in the space of three days!

But the journey to and from the capital cities was proving extremely wasteful of time, and in 1874 a depot was established at Somerset near the tip of Cape York Peninsula, and then in 1878 the centre of operations was transferred to Thursday Island, which has remained the base of the Barrier Reef and Torres Strait fishery to the present day.

At the present time there are eight companies operating at Thursday Island; all are capitalized and controlled in Australia.

The boats consist principally of luggers built locally and costing from £1500 to £2000; they are graceful and sturdy craft of from fifteen to twenty tons, an average length of about fifty feet, and a draught of from seven to ten feet. Until quite recently many of these luggers were dependent on sailing power only, but all boats are now fitted with auxiliary engines which serve not only to propel them when necessary but also to work the compressors that supply air to the divers.

Fishing is carried on only during the period of neap tides, for the great rise and fall of spring tides, averaging about fifteen feet, is accompanied by strong currents that stir up the bottom and render the water cloudy. During this period, therefore, the boats return to their base at Thursday Island to unload their shell and revictual. The neap tides usually last on the Torres Strait grounds from six to ten days and in the vicinity of Darwin from three to six days.

The luggers are in charge of either a Japanese or a Malayan diver who receives £3 per month and his keep, with a bonus of £22/10/- per ton on all the shell lifted by the boat. The crews vary in number from six to nine; they consist of Malays, Japanese, and Torres Strait Islanders, and are victualled and paid by the master pearlers. For a considerable time after the inception of the industry many Australian aborigines were employed on the luggers but for the most part they did not give satisfactory service and they have now been completely eliminated. All boats are fitted with air-compressors which allow of two divers working at the same time.

When the lugger arrives at the ground where fishing is contemplated, one of the crew takes a sounding with lead and line. The line is marked off in fathoms and to the extremity of the lead is attached a small piece of soap or tallow; when this touches the sea-floor some of the bottom deposit sticks to it and its nature may thereby be determined. Should the examination show that the bottom is of such a character that shell is likely to be found, the lugger is immediately luffed up and a diver goes overboard while the boat, carrying jib and mainsail, drifts at a speed of from one to two knots. For a while the diver may drift a few feet above the bottom till he sees some shell when he signals to be lowered, and for the rest of the drift his feet usually drag over the surface in order to keep him on a straight course. Should he see an obstacle, such as a large boulder, in his path, he closes the outlet valve, thereby filling the suit with air, which enables him to float over the obstacle, and when clear of it he lets the air out and descends gently on the other side. As he collects the shell he places it in a net, which holds about fifty-six pounds of shell. Should a rich ground be encountered the lugger is signalled and a buoy is immediately dropped over and anchored to the bottom; the boat then moves round in circles in order to allow the diver to recover as much shell as possible from the limited area.

There are several classes of ground on which pearl-shell is found; the most common consists of coral, and the shell in such situations generally lies on the surface; next in importance is sand and shell-grit in which the shell is usually found slightly embedded; then the shell may be found on ironstone gravel; and lastly, in the vicinity of Darnley and other islands on the east of Torres Strait the shell lies on a volcanic bottom where it may be found on the surface, under ledges, or in the vicinity of giant boulders. Pearl-shell is never found on a muddy bottom.

The depth fished varies from about six to thirty fathoms. It is known that rich beds exist below thirty fathoms and in May 1936 a new type of diving dress was introduced to the Darwin grounds which, it is claimed, will allow a diver to descend to a depth of sixty fathoms and beyond and to rise to the surface without the "staging" necessary with the ordinary form of dress. It is well known, of course, that with the ordinary diving suit if a diver descends to a depth below ten fathoms he must be brought to the surface in easy stages in order to avoid the risk of paralysis, the duration of the staging depending on the depth and the length of time the diver has been below. If a diver has been working at fifteen fathoms for an hour it will take from thirty to thirty-five minutes to bring him to the surface; if he has been working at twenty-five fathoms for half an hour, his ascent will take about two and a half hours. Moreover, the length of time he may stay below decreases as the depth increases; at fifteen fathoms he is limited to about an hour and a half. With the new diving dress it is claimed that the diver may rise to the surface from a depth of sixty fathoms in two and a half minutes without suffering any ill-effects. The helmet of this suit is provided with valves which allow the air to be released into the suit at ordinary atmospheric pressure.

If extensive use can be made of this suit many rich grounds of great extent will become available for commercial exploitation, and the cost of recovering the shell will be cheapened very considerably for the diver will be able to remain below for indefinite periods and no time will be lost

PLATE 48.

BLUE-SPOTTED GROPER
A coral fish of excellent edible quality which grows to a length of upwards of three feet.

RED MOUTHED EMPEROR
A fine food fish caught by line on the bottom.

in bringing him to the surface. It is stated that in 1935 a diver clad in this dress descended to a depth of forty fathoms off Darnley Island and filled his bag with shell from an area of a few square yards.

Pearling is a hazardous occupation. The diver's career is usually ended at forty, and every year witnesses its crop of casualties. Risks are run whether the diver is working naked in shallow water, when he is exposed to the attacks of sharks and giant groper, or whether he is working in a diving-suit, when his air-line may be fouled by a groper or a devil ray, or he may when on a rich ground stay below longer than is safe, or, perhaps, lured by the abundance of shell in deep water he may exceed a depth below the safety zone and, coming to the surface at too great a speed, arrive there crippled with paralysis.

Now, there is a prevalent impression that sharks will not attack black people; this may have been gained by the nonchalant manner in which black boys dive for coins in shark-infested waters when passenger boats lie at anchor. Unfortunately there is no truth in it, for sharks will and all too frequently do attack native divers, and at least six cases have been recorded on the pearling and trochus grounds during the past three years. In 1933 a Torres Strait islander was badly mauled by a shark; in 1934 a New Guinea diver lost his life from the same cause, and in 1935 four divers were attacked but three of them fortunately recovered. When attired in a diving-suit attacks are extremely rare, and I remember only one report of such an occurrence. On the approach of a shark the diver usually opens wide the valve which allows the air to escape; the rush of bubbles scares the shark and it rapidly makes away.

Probably the most extraordinary of all recorded shark attacks occurred in 1914 when a Thursday Island native,

Q

known familiarly as "Treacle" or "Teapot," suddenly found his head inside a shark's jaws; its teeth gripped him tightly round the neck and caused a dreadful wound, but apparently as the shark opened its mouth to gulp him he pulled his head away and, swimming frantically, effected his escape. He was rushed to hospital, where he remained for a month under treatment, and eventually recovered! A photograph of this native is reproduced in Plate 44, fig. 1; it was taken as he was convalescing in the hospital, and shows prominently the scars on his neck left by the shark's great teeth.

Although the records show that attacks by giant groper, which frequently grow to a weight of several hundredweight, are much less common than those by sharks, the divers fear them no less, for they are more insidious in their methods and are less easily scared. They may lurk in a dark cavern and rush the diver before he is aware of their approach, or they may stalk him with great persistence, undeterred by the rush of bubbles to the surface.

But there are many other risks. An extremely unusual fatality was reported in 1935 when a Japanese diver, working in about twenty fathoms on pearling-grounds about fifty miles north-west of Bathurst Island in Torres Strait, suddenly felt a stinging pain in his hand as he was about to gather a shell; withdrawing his hand quickly he found a great sea-snake, which his companion diver estimated to be about eight feet long, clinging to it; in vain he tried to shake it off, and it was only by tugging with his other hand that he eventually freed it. Signalling his distress, he was drawn to the surface but died an hour or two afterwards.

Sea-snakes are very common in these waters, though they are seldom found beyond a length of two or three feet; all are very venomous, but they will rarely attack unless molested. Apparently this was a stray from Indo-Malayan waters, where they grow to a much greater size.

Although the divers in diving-dress run very little risk from such attacks, their casualties from paralysis are fairly heavy. When working at a depth of, say, eighteen to twenty fathoms the pressure of water is very great, and unless the diver is brought to the surface in easy stages, the sudden reduction of pressure liberates gases in the blood, and, interfering with the circulation to the brain, causes paralysis. Should this occur, the diver is again lowered for lengthy periods, possibly several hours each day for several days, when recovery may sometimes be effected. Occasionally a diver may suddenly collapse and die when actually at work in these depths, and every year sees its casualties from this cause. During 1935 there were four such casualties amongst the Japanese divers working the beds off Darnley Island in Torres Strait; the shell was abundant in deep water, and it is said that the divers took the risk of venturing into water as deep as thirty fathoms, with tragic results.

The hazards of the pearl-divers are not confined to the actual diving. Two vessels were lost in curious circumstances in 1922 off Cape York Peninsula; they were caught up in great water spouts and swamped before rescue could reach them and all hands were lost. Cyclones of tremendous fury are always a possibility in the summer months and, springing up with great suddenness, may catch a fleet entirely unawares. In 1934, for instance, two luggers were lost in a cyclonic disturbance off the north-eastern Queensland coast with the loss of thirteen of the crew, including three Japanese, five Papuans, and five Australian aborigines. The most serious tragedy from this cause, however, occurred in 1899 when a large pearling fleet was working newly discovered ground in Princess Charlotte Bay on the eastern side of Cape York Peninsula. Suddenly, without warning, the whole fleet was caught in a hurricane of intense fury; boat after boat was dashed to pieces on the rocks near Cape Melville till fifty-four of them were lost and twelve white and two hundred and ninety-five coloured men were drowned.

One who has not been caught in the throes of a tropical cyclone can form little idea of its severity. I once had such an experience and it will live for ever in my memory. It was in February, 1929, when at the invitation of Professor Johannes Schmidt I accompanied the Danish research trawler, *Dana*, on a trip from Sydney to Brisbane. During the voyage north the barometer was particularly high and when about one hundred and fifty miles east of Brisbane it fell with great suddenness; the wind, previously from the north-east, swung round to the east, then to the south-east, and finally to the south. In a short time it was blowing at eighty miles an hour. For two days and nights we plugged against it under easy steam, now descending into a great trough, now ploughing our way up to the crest. Battened down, the air was hot and stifling, and as time wore on the stuffiness of the cabins became appalling, till at length it was almost unbearable; we were all gasping for breath, and in desperation a port-hole was opened when a column of water shot into the small dining-saloon on the main deck and flooded it. Yet there was no relief on deck; one could not withstand the force of the seas that swept continually over it, while the effect of the screeching wind, blowing the tops of enormous rollers into spray and carrying it along for hundreds of yards, was not pleasant to look upon. We had no idea where we were, but during the course of the second night the echo-sounder, which gave an instantaneous record of the depth of the water below us, caused a consternation when it registered a hundred and twenty yards.

PLATE 49.

HARLEQUIN SMILER
A coral fish that grows to a length of about fifteen inches.

RED-BANDED CORAL FISH

What had happened? When the cyclone first hit us we were a hundred and fifty miles from land, in water about a mile and a half deep. The instrument was now watched incessantly; gradually the water became shallower—eighty yards, fifty, thirty. Although steering a compass course due south, we were clearly being carried by the current towards the shore. Suddenly through the heavy rain a light flashed close to us; we were alongside the Cape Byron light in New South Wales and, turning, we again made north. But worse was to come. The great seas following us would hit the stern of the boat and come crashing, hundreds of tons of them, on deck; the boat would stagger under the weight, and every instant we expected to be swamped. How long could it withstand this tremendous pounding? And so through the night this battering continued and not a minute's sleep was obtained by a soul on board.

Then, as suddenly as it began, the wind abated and when dawn broke a bright sun was shining on the waters; they had lost their fury and heaved, as it were, with exhaustion from their mighty efforts. Thoroughly relieved at our escape we gathered on deck and discussed our various feelings; all were agreed that the echo-sounder had saved our lives. And so we celebrated by drinking to the old Viking toast, "Min Skaal, din Skaal, alle smukke Pigers Skaal" (Here's to me, and to you, and to every pretty girl).

What chance would a fleet of pearlers have in a wind and sea like that?

But we must return to them. With holds filled, or perhaps only partially filled if they have been working on poor ground, the luggers return to Thursday Island. There, until a few years ago, the shell after sorting (Plate 43, fig. 1), was sold by tender, with British and United States buyers the principal operators, and the world's markets were able to absorb the whole of the supplies. With the advent of the depression, however, the demand fell away greatly, and in 1930 overseas buyers were forced to curtail their operations. In conference with the Torres Strait Pearlsellers' Association at Thursday Island it was agreed that production would be restricted during 1930 to 850 tons, as a result of which twenty-two vessels relinquished fishing for pearl-shell and seven of them were refitted for the trochus industry. This came at a particularly unfortunate time, for a rich bed had been discovered in 1928 north-west of Wallace Islands; this had proved to be the most important discovery for many years, and during the first two months of operations many of the vessels won more shell than they had gathered during the previous twelve months. Record yields were obtained, and it was estimated that 1400 tons of shell were lifted from this ground during the 1929 season, constituting a record production for any one year since the inception of the industry. This was about 800 tons above the average, and it left a carry-over for the following season at a time when the market slumped so greatly.

Worse was to follow. In 1931 the restriction agreed upon was 350 tons; during 1932 and 1933 this was raised to 460 tons; and in 1934 and 1935 to 750 tons. The restrictions were serious enough, but the price during those years receded to an unprofitable level, averaging in 1935 only £106 per ton, the whole of the output going under contract to a company in New York. The number of boats engaged in the gathering of pearl-shell, which in 1929 numbered a hundred and twenty-nine, decreased yearly till in 1935 only eighty-nine remained, and a number of these were employed for a part only of the season. This, of course, meant a great loss not only to the owners, but also to the crews; in 1931 alone several hundred indented employees were returned to their native countries.

It will profit us now to review briefly the history of this industry. From a modest beginning in 1868, when only one boat operated, the production increased rapidly each year till in 1897 a record harvest of 1233 tons was obtained. From that date till the outbreak of the world war in 1914 the catch gradually declined; in 1904 it was reduced to 778 tons, in 1909 to 516 tons, and in 1913 to 466 tons. Then the war put a stop to diving and the production fell away almost to nothing. With this enforced inactivity the beds, which had become less and less productive through overfishing, were given an opportunity to recover, and the production when diving was resumed rose rapidly; from 1925 to 1930 inclusive, the thousand-ton mark was exceeded every year but one, when in 1927 it fell short by seventy-eight tons. And then followed the depression with a very marked decline in the demand; this was accompanied by keen competition from cheaper articles which were made to serve the purpose for which pearl-shell had in the past been used so extensively.

And now, what of the future? At the moment of writing (October 1936) the outlook appears brighter than for several years; surplus stocks have been disposed of, restrictions on the output have been lifted, and the price has risen to £150 per ton. With the gradual lifting of the depression, the pearl-shell industry of the Barrier Reef promises to return to more prosperous days.

The bulk of the Australian market for goods of a pearl-shell origin is supplied by an industry which in 1930 was established in Sydney. The manufacture of pearl-shell buttons in Australia actually dates from about 1885 when a small factory was opened in Sydney, but it operated for only a few years.

The buttons are cut from the shell by means of a rapidly-revolving tubular saw, the "blanks" as they are termed, being cut as closely as possible in order to reduce the wastage of the shell to a minimum (Plate 43, fig. 2). These blanks are split to the required thickness by a sharp tap on a keen-edged tool; this is the only operation performed by hand, and it is rendered necessary because of the variation in the "grain" of the shell. Both surfaces of the blanks are ground perfectly flat by friction against a revolving emery wheel, and one surface is then fashioned to the required design and shape on a turning lathe by means of profiling tools. After fashioning, two or four holes are drilled with absolute precision about the centre by means of a rapidly-revolving needle in a machine that is capable of drilling forty gross of buttons per day.

The buttons are now ready for polishing. This consists of two processes, the first mechanical, the second chemical. They are placed in drums or "rumblers" with water and a little pumice powder and the drums are revolved for several hours till the surfaces of the buttons are quite smooth. They are then boiled in soapy water and treated with muriatic (hydrochloric) acid and bluestone (copper sulphate) to increase their lustre and render it permanent. After washing they are given a final polishing in a felt-lined drum and are then ready for sorting and grading, and sewing on to cards. They are sorted into three qualities according to their degree of whiteness and freedom from blemishes.

The thicker part of the shell near the hinge is known in the trade as the "knuckle"; it is very hard and can be split only in rare cases, and it is therefore mostly used for fancy articles such a knife-handles, cigarette-holders, sleeve-links, spoons, and butter-knives.

Articles made from pearl-shell may be dyed without destroying the lustre, but their beauty lies in the delicacy of their lustre rather than in their colour, and it is doubtful whether any advantage is gained by dyeing them.

The smaller black-lip pearl-shell is occasionally used in the manufacture of buttons and buckles, but the demand for such articles, on account of their dark colour, is very restricted and consequently the quantity produced is never very great.

The average quantity of pearl-shell produced annually from the Great Barrier Reef area during the ten years from 1926 to 1935 inclusive amounted to 889 tons, valued at £122,992, or £140 per ton.

"PEARL" BUTTONS FROM TROCHUS SHELLS

If you examine the pearl buttons you are wearing you will possibly see that the rougher under surface is streaked with red, brown, or green; if so you are wearing, not buttons made from real pearl-shell, but from the shell known as trochus, the gathering of which forms the second largest industry of the Barrier Reef.

It is an industry of comparatively recent origin. As the pearl-shell fishermen combed the Barrier in the early days of the industry they saw on many of the reefs these cone-shaped shells in great profusion, but passed them by with scarcely a second glance. Just prior to 1912, however, some trial shipments were forwarded to Austria and Japan in order to determine whether the thick mother-of-pearl that composed their shells was capable of being manufactured into buttons. This, it was found, presented no difficulty, and consequently in 1912 thirty-five tons of the shells were shipped abroad for that purpose.

But the market for real pearl-shell was firmly established and the production of trochus shells for the three following years showed only a small increase. Then the diving for pearl-shell was prohibited owing to the mining of parts of the coast as a war-time precaution, and the luggers were diverted to the collection of trochus shell, which could be obtained in large quantities by searchers wandering over the various reefs at low tide. As a result the trochus-shell industry increased enormously and in 1916, 1048 tons were marketed; this amount has only once been surpassed when, in 1927, 1080 tons were produced.

The trochus, or "troca," as it is frequently termed by the Torres Strait islanders and the natives of northern Queensland, is a cone-shaped shell wider across the circular base than its height, and when seen on the reef is usually a dull yellowish-green or brown, but after the thin external coating is removed the shell is found to be attractively marked with crimson or reddish-brown stripes. It grows to a width of about five and a half inches and a height of about four inches, but the average width of those marketed is from three to four inches. Young shells are known in the trade as "chicken" shells and bring an inferior price, while the very large ones are usually rejected owing to the deterioration of the shell from various causes.

The trochus shell is found right throughout the Great Barrier Reef area, from Torres Strait to as far south as Swain Reefs, which form the southern limit of the true Barrier. In the early days of the industry the shells occurred so prolifically on the reef flats that great quantities were collected by simply wandering over the reef when the tide was out, but after a few years the shell gatherers were forced farther afield till now the bulk of the supplies is obtained by divers working in the comparatively shallow water a short distance beyond the reef edge. The shell is not found in deep water, the limit of its depth being about seven fathoms.

The boats used (cutters and luggers) are exactly similar

to those engaged in the pearling industry. With Thursday Island as their base the boats, with three or four dinghies stowed on board, proceed to the grounds intended to be worked; on arrival there the dinghies are lowered and the native crews row them to the various parts of the reef. On account of the comparatively shallow water diving-suits are not used; the natives are clad only in a pair of water-goggles made to fit tightly about the eyes, and, carrying a bag to hold the trochus, they dive overboard and swim to the bottom, where they remain usually about two minutes.

After some hours' diving the crews return to the luggers, and the shells are boiled in a large cylindrical boiler, when the animal inside the shell shrinks and on cooling is easily extracted. The meat itself may be eaten by the aboriginal crews, or it may be smoked for sale when the lugger returns to Thursday Island; it brings about £60 per ton, and is exported to China and Singapore, where it is converted into soups and stews.

On returning to Thursday Island the shell is spread out and submitted for tender, practically the whole output being subsequently forwarded to Japan.

Many of the trochus luggers are owned by the companies engaged in the pearling-industry, but about half the total output is produced by Torres Strait islanders who own, or are paying off, their own boats, each member of the crew receiving payment for so much of the catch as he was responsible for. The whole scheme of recruiting labour, marketing, and care of the financial side of the operations is under Government supervision, the natives are for the most part happy and contented, and they frequently make good money.

In Japan the dealers farm the shells out to the workers, who cut out and prepare the buttons in their own homes, the whole family at times assisting in the various operations, and payment is made according to the quantity produced. The operations are essentially similar to those used in the manufacture of buttons from pearl-shell described on page 232; the operators cut out the circular "blanks" by means of a small cylindrical tool with a saw-like edge revolving at high speed, the whorls of the shell being followed from above downwards; the "blanks" are split to the required thickness; holes are drilled through their centres; and they are then polished and sewn on cards. With this form of labour other countries cannot compete with Japan, and it would appear that that country will continue to monopolize the industry.

Trochus-shell buttons sell at a considerably lower price than pearl-shell buttons; they are of inferior quality, for their lasting qualities are not nearly so good, and they tend to turn yellow after repeated boilings.

Although during recent years the quantity of trochus shell produced in the Barrier Reef area has been maintained at a fairly constant level, there was a considerable drop during the five-year period from 1930 to 1934 compared with that of the preceding five years. From 1925 to 1929 the average annual production amounted to 873 tons, whereas during the following five years it averaged only 518 tons, and this supply was only maintained through the marketing of increased quantities of smaller shell.

The price received during the first year of production was only £17 per ton; it gradually rose, however, till in 1920 the record price of £90 per ton was obtained, and since that time it has fluctuated between £41 and £80, the average price for the five-year period between 1930 and 1934 being £69 per ton.

It is obvious that the indiscriminate gathering of the shell

PLATE 50.

SUNLIGHT AND SHADE AMONG THE PANDANUS-TREES,
WILSON ISLAND

THE CLOSE OF DAY, HERON ISLAND

has been responsible for considerable depletion of available supplies, and during the stay of the British Barrier Reef Expedition at Low Island and subsequently, Mr F. W. Moorhouse carried out an investigation into the life-history of the animal, with the ultimate object of placing the control of the industry on a sound scientific basis. Moorhouse found that at the end of one year a trochus shell is approximately one inch in diameter at the base, and that it grows at the rate of about an inch per year. It reaches maturity when it is from two to two and a half inches in diameter, and breeds throughout practically the whole of the winter. Its food consists of fine seaweeds which it scrapes off the coral rocks.

Now, it is necessary, in any attempt to maintain the supplies of a marine animal, that every individual taken from the water should have had an opportunity of spawning at least once, and the history of the world's fisheries has provided abundant evidence that ultimate depletion is inevitable if continued inroads are made on immature individuals. In view of Moorhouse's findings the Queensland Government in 1932 prohibited the taking of trochus shell under two and a half inches in diameter. It is presumed, therefore, that every individual marketed in the future will have spawned once and if this restricton is rigidly adhered to (as, of course, it should be), then there should be no difficulty in maintaining supplies at their present level. If, however, signs of further depletion are evident in the near future, owing possibly to a lack of uniformity of the size reached at maturity in various parts of the reef, it may become necessary to increase the restriction to three inches, at least over that area where maturity is reached when the size of the shell is greater than that at present determined. On a question such as this there can be no compromise.

A striking illustration of the value of restrictive legislation based on accurate information of the size of an animal when it reaches sexual maturity has been furnished by the crab industry of California. About twenty years ago this industry was found to be declining rapidly and an investigation of the breeding-habits of the crab was decided upon. It was found that the then minimum size limit of six inches was too low since it permitted the destruction of male crabs before they had a chance to breed, and legislation was enacted which raised the size limit to seven inches. The result of so small a change was remarkable. A few years after passing the new regulation, when the first crop of crabs under its protection had reached the seven-inch size, the production of the fishery suddenly doubled, and since then the catch has gone on increasing until in 1933 the fishery produced 75,000 dozen more than it did before the law was changed, an increase worth £37,000 to the fishermen. Yet originally these fishermen opposed the change, protesting that already at six inches the size limit was too high, and that declining production could be stayed only by permitting the capture of smaller individuals through the reduction of the six-inch limit. And so scientific investigation, backed by a realization of its value, gained a wonderful triumph over popular opinion and the "experience" of the fishermen.

The trochus shell is by no means exclusively a product of Barrier Reef waters. It occurs also in the East Indies, the Philippines, New Guinea, New Caledonia, and other islands of the Pacific. New Caledonia produces large quantities and about fifteen hundred men are employed in the industry in those waters.

The average quantity of trochus shell produced annually from the Great Barrier Reef during the ten years from

1926 to 1935 inclusive amounted to 677 tons, valued at £51,647, or £73 per ton.

THE BÊCHE-DE-MER INDUSTRY

When I was a boy some companions and I decided to go camping. We hired a tent, prepared the necessary equipment, and with light hearts set out for our destination. On arrival there the duties incidental to preparing camp were allotted by majority vote, and for some reason which I was never told and which I never discovered I was elected cook. While the others were busy cutting saplings and erecting the tent I made a long journey to the nearest butcher and bought what I regarded as probably the simplest of all culinary dishes—pork sausages. The butcher also persuaded me to buy some dripping; I thought that this was quite an unnecessary expense and that the butcher was probably overstocked with the greasy commodity. However, he duly succeeded in convincing me that no good chef would think of frying sausages without its help and, extracting another sixpence from my slender resources, he handed it to me in quite a neat parcel with strict instructions not to squeeze it too tightly.

On my return to the camp I immediately set about preparing lunch. After much scratching about I built a rough fireplace and in a very short time a blaze worthy of Vulcan himself was leaping skyward. The sausages were grouped about the frying-pan, the dripping duly added, and in a few seconds the whole began to sizzle in the most approved style. At least I had succeeded in making a wonderful fire; so high leaped the flames that my eyebrows singed—and unfortunately for my reputation as a cook—so did the sausages. To my amazement they shrank, and shrank, and shrivelled and split until I came to the conclusion that the butcher had sold me, not sausages at all, but balloons which on the first prick of the fork, collapsed.

Now, if you have ever been guilty of the atrocity of frying sausages over a hot fire you will have a fairly good idea what bêche-de-mer looks like when prepared for the Chinese market; only it is larger, of course, and as dry as a bone (Plate 10, fig. 2).

The bêche-de-mer ranks next in importance to the trochus as a commercial product of the Great Barrier Reef. It occurs in many varieties and in extremely prolific numbers throughout the whole reef area, but a few kinds only are of commercial importance. Everywhere you wander over a reef at low tide, whether it be east of Torres Strait or in the Bunker Group of islands situated at its southern extremity, bêche-de-mer will be found always amongst the most prominent objects of the reef flats. Few of these are of any value; they are usually too small and their flesh is not sufficiently thick to warrant their collection for market.

The boats used in the bêche-de-mer industry are similar to those engaged in pearling; they usually combine the gathering of bêche-de-mer and trochus, and all are fitted with smoke-houses necessary for the preparation of the product for market. Some are owned by Australian companies who usually employ Japanese skippers with mixed crews of Australian aborigines, Torres Strait, and South Sea islanders; others are owned and directed by Torres Strait islanders who carry on their operations, as was pointed out when describing the trochus industry, under Government supervision.

The boat anchors off a reef and the blacks may gather their supplies by wading about the shallow water on the reef flat, or they may dive into the deeper water beyond the reef crest where the most valuable varieties are usually found.

But many of these occur in water up to seven or eight fathoms and they are then gathered in an entirely different manner. The natives construct a small "telescope" consisting of a rectangular box about two feet deep and eight or nine inches square; glass is let into the base which is held just beneath the surface of the water enabling the bottom to be seen clearly at a depth of at least sixty feet. As soon as an animal of value is sighted a line with a heavy, barbed spear-point at the end of it is let down and the creature dexterously transfixed, or "pinned" as it is frequently termed, and it is then hauled to the surface.

When the animals are brought to the lugger they are boiled in an iron vessel for twenty minutes to half an hour, and when cool are split open lengthwise by means of a sharp knife, and gutted. They are then usually left in the sun for a time to dry, the larger ones being kept open by inserting small pegs in their interior. When sufficiently dry they are ready for the smoke-house. This consists of a rectangular enclosure, usually of galvanized iron, fitted with wire-netting trays in the upper portion; the bêche-de-mer are arranged on these trays and a fire lighted beneath them, the wood most favoured being the red mangrove. Smoking takes about twenty-four hours and when completed the animals, now hard, wrinkled, and shrunken to less than half their original size (remember those sausages), may again be placed in the sun to ensure complete dryness, which is absolutely essential if they are to remain in perfect condition. When thoroughly dry, bêche-de-mer will keep indefinitely, so long as it is not allowed to become damp. The specimens illustrated in Plate 10, fig. 2 had suffered no deterioration in spite of the fact that they were prepared over thirty years ago.

R

When sufficient has been obtained the lugger returns to Thursday Island where Chinese buyers await their coming; they are shipped direct to China, the principal distributing centre being Hong Kong. Chinese steeped in the culinary art prepare from these most uninviting objects soups famed for their delicate flavour; if the soup is made, however, by simply boiling them it is rather tasteless and unattractive, they are therefore used as stock and their ultimate preparation may be of quite an elaborate character.

The different kinds of bêche-de-mer are known in the trade under curious but long-established names and their value varies enormously. For instance, we have, in the ascending order of their value, chalk fish, lolly fish, sand fish, tiger fish, prickly fish, small black fish, red fish, teat fish, and deepwater black fish, the value of which ranges from about £30 to over £300 per ton, the average price over the last ten years (1926-35) being £93 per ton. During that period the average annual production amounted to 213 tons, varying from 139 tons in 1935 to 441 tons in 1932; the price received averaged £19,240 and varied from £12,688 in 1926 to £29,383 in 1927. The demand fluctuates very greatly and is dependent largely on Chinese internal affairs which, of course, have been subject to much unrest during decent years.

The future of the industry seems to be almost entirely dependent on the buying capabilities of China. In spite of the fact that the bêche-de-mer fishery is by far the oldest established of any carried on in the Great Barrier Reef area, the available supplies show little signs of serious depletion; indeed, there is no doubt that the output could be increased very considerably, if the demand warranted it, without great prejudice to the future of the industry.

THE FISHING INDUSTRY OF THE BARRIER

The capture of edible fish in the great expanse of water enclosed by the Great Barrier Reef is an industry of considerable importance and will probably expand greatly with the introduction of modern and efficient methods of refrigeration which will allow of the wider distribution of the fish without appreciable deterioration.

The types of fish caught fall naturally into two classes—those which inhabit the surface waters (pelagic fish) and those which frequent the bottom (demersal fish).

Of the pelagic fish the striped Spanish mackerel is by far the most important. As we have seen in the chapter on angling, this fine fish, although found in the vicinity of the outer barrier throughout the whole of the year, congregates in great shoals only during the winter months, and it is during that period that the fishery for its capture is most intense and widespread. During May and June it is found in greatest abundance in the southern areas of the reef, and during those months the professional fishermen engaged in its capture are to be found amongst the coral islands of the Bunker and Capricorn groups, the fish being taken to Gladstone where they are frozen for distribution mainly to Rockhampton and Brisbane. As the shoals work north the fishermen follow them, and in July and August they are most active amongst the mainland islands of the Cumberland and Whitsunday groups. The fish continue their northward migration and during late winter and spring considerable numbers are landed at Townsville and Cairns. Portion of the supply is sold at the port of landing, the surplus being distributed to adjacent towns and to Brisbane which receives its largest consignments from Gladstone, Mackay, and Townsville.

The Spanish mackerel is regarded as one of the finest

edible fish in Queensland waters, and it has the added advantage of smoking particularly well; indeed, it is doubtful whether it is surpassed in this condition by any other fish from Australian waters. It grows to a length of at least six feet and a weight of upwards of a hundred pounds, the average weight being from twenty-five to thirty-five pounds. The methods adopted by the professional fishermen to capture it are in marked contrast to those of the amateur anglers— their objective is the landing of the greatest quantity in the shortest possible time and tackle is used which will allow of the fish being pulled straight to the boat. The fishing boats vary from twenty-five to forty feet in length and the crew consists usually of three; one takes charge of the boat while the other two fish. Mackerel will bite a moving bait only and they are therefore caught by trolling a bait or lure behind the launch. Hand-lines of cord or heavy gut are used; they are baited with garfish if supplies are obtainable or with lures or even rags if garfish are not to be had. At times the boat fishing for mackerel may be fitted with "outriggers" in the form of long poles fastened to the mast and projecting well out over the water, one on each side. A line is trolled from the tip of each pole while two and sometimes three lines are held by the fishermen at the stern of the boat. When amongst a school of fish the men may be forced to work with feverish activity for the baits are frequently taken faster than the fish can be hauled in.

Occasionally, when in a densely congregated shoal, the boat may be anchored and the baits thrown well astern to be immediately hauled in, the fish grabbing the bait as it moves towards the boat. When properly "on the bite" mackerel take the bait ravenously.

As soon as there is a lull in the operations the fish are

gutted, washed, and stored between intermediate layers of crushed ice in the ice-box which may be capable of holding upwards of a ton of fish. About a ton of ice is usually carried on each trip.

Although the main objective of these fishermen is the striped Spanish mackerel, a number of other large pelagic fish may be caught during the course of trolling. These include spotted mackerel; queenfish or leatherskin (mackerel-like in shape but closely related to the trevally); turrum and other giant trevallies; kingfish; tunny; pike; albacore; bonito; tailor; and an occasional marlin swordfish.

If pelagic fish cannot be located the fishermen may anchor or drift for the capture of reef fish, though these are frequently caught from boats which fish for them exclusively. In this branch of the fishery, also, greater activity is displayed during the winter, for not only then do the fish bite more freely, but there is much less difficulty in keeping the fish in good condition for market.

Hand-lines of either gut or cord are used from a boat that may be moored or allowed to drift over the channels between growths of coral. Fish of a wide variety of species are taken by this means, and most of them are of excellent edible quality. There is a prevalent impression that the best edible fish come from latitudes where the water is always cold; that for this reason the fishes of the North Sea, for instance, are superior to those of New South Wales and Queensland; that those from Tasmania are of finer flavour than those from Australian tropical waters. Of course, on the question of flavour there can never be unanimity of opinion, but of this I am personally convinced, there are many fishes of the Great Barrier Reef that for both flavour and texture are unsurpassed by any to be found elsewhere on the Australian coast. The Tasmanian trumpeter is a fish of extraordinarily fine flavour, but is it superior to the pearl perch, the red emperor, the spotted Spanish mackerel, or the coral cod of the Barrier Reef? Most epicures would agree, I think, that it is not.

Most of the reef fish caught for market vary from about five to twenty pounds in weight though occasionally much larger fish may be captured, including that veritable giant, the Queensland groper, a fish that is badly named for it is in no way related to the gropers of the other States but is a member of the family of perches. Excluding the sword-fishes and marlins the Queensland groper is probably the largest of all bony fishes; it has been known to attain a weight of seven hundred pounds, and specimens of two or three hundredweight are fairly common. Such large individuals are coarse and tough but young ones, up to thirty or forty pounds, are excellent eating.

A near relative of the Queensland groper, and frequently confused with it, is the black rock cod which grows to a weight of about a hundred pounds. It is common and widespread, and when young is a delicious table fish.

Amongst the most abundant of the reef fish may be mentioned the red emperor which grows to a weight of eighty pounds; sweetlips of several species; snapper up to thirty pounds; coral or slate bream up to thirty-five pounds; coral cod up to forty pounds (Plate 47, fig. 1); king snapper (Plate 47, fig. 2); coral trout; yellow-banded hussar; red-mouthed emperor (Plate 48, fig. 2); several species of wrasses and parrot-fishes, including the blue-spotted groper (Plate 48, fig. 1) and the "blue-bone" or "blue-tooth"; and, south of North-West Island, the pearl perch or epaulette fish which grows to a weight of about ten pounds and is one of the finest edible fish found in Australian waters.

There is a branch of the Barrier Reef fisheries that can

scarcely yet be said to have been touched—the capture of small pelagic fish such as herrings, pilchards, sprats and hardyheads, and it is difficult to assess their potential value for the reason that, with the exception of a recent and unsuccessful attempt to exploit the small herrings that are found in abundance in the vicinity of Murray Island, no endeavour has been made to capture them commercially, and consequently little is known of their movements or of the regularity of their occurrence in Barrier Reef waters. That they are at times extremely abundant is apparent to any one who spends any length of time cruising over those waters, for over wide areas these fish will frequently be seen breaking the surface of the water and causing it to appear as if a great shower of hail were falling on it. Further evidence of their abundance is indicated by the fact that they provide the principal food of the myriads of birds that nest on many of the islands of the reef during the summer months. It has been estimated, as we have seen, that on North-West Island alone from one to two million mutton-birds and about half that number of noddy terns inhabit the island during the summer-time, and on many other islands they are equally prolific; these birds feed on small surface-swimming fish and the enormous quantities consumed can readily be realized. It is expected that much light will be thrown on the occurrence, abundance, and economics generally of these fish by the investigations of the Commonwealth fisheries research vessel, *Warreen*, which was designed particularly for the capture of pelagic fish.

THE COMMERCIAL PRODUCTS OF THE SHARK

Sharks are abundant right throughout the Great Barrier Reef area, but their exploitation commercially is dependent on a sufficient regularity of supplies. They are also prevalent on the coast of New South Wales, but, although one or two serious attempts have been made to exploit them, none has yet succeeded in developing into a financially successful industry.

There is no question of the value of the products yielded; the hide can be converted into an excellent leather, pliable, handsome, and durable; the oil from the liver is in demand in certain industries; the fins are always saleable in China where they are converted into a soup much prized by their epicures; the flesh may be dried and exported to the East where there is a market for it, or it may be converted into meal, of value as an added diet for cattle, poultry, and pigs.

Of these the hide is the most valuable. In order to remove it the tail is chopped off, the fins are removed, and the skin is slit straight along the back with a sharp knife (the cut must not extend as far as the pores which show as minute holes on the head), and then the knife is run downwards travelling back behind the gills and then forward on each side within an inch or two of the lower jaw. The hide is now cut away from the flesh, care being taken that the skin itself is not cut. When the hide is removed it is laid on a beaming board, in the form of a curved upright iron frame, and the surplus flesh carefully trimmed off. After a thorough washing in salt water to remove any adherent blood or slime the hide is ready for salting or curing; it is laid flesh side upwards on an incline in order to allow the water to drain off, and the surface is covered with a liberal sprinkling of coarse butcher's salt; another hide is laid over this and the salting repeated; and so on.

Curing takes from about eight days to a fortnight, depending largely on the thickness of the hide and the weather; during the process the hides must be kept indoors away from the sun and the rain. When thoroughly cured the hides are shaken lightly to remove surplus salt and fresh, dry salt is sprinkled over the surface; they are then folded into flat, square bundles and shipped in barrels or other suitable containers to the tanner.

On receipt by the tanner the first operation consists of the removal of the denticles or shagreen that cover the external surface. The hides are placed in a liquid consisting of a saturated solution of salt in a ten per cent solution of hydrochloric acid and are allowed to remain there till the denticles dissolve away, usually at the end of about two hours. Frequently patches of denticles remain loosely adherent to the hides, but these can be removed by scraping the surface with the square edge of a board. The acid in the hides is now neutralized by means of lime and they are then ready for tanning in the same manner as bullock hides, either in a vegetable or chrome tan liquor. When tanned they can be dyed or sprayed with a cellulose lacquer to any desired colour. During the course of tanning, the surface of the hide develops a very pleasing, somewhat coarse grain which is characteristic only of shark hide. About eighty square feet of leather is produced from a ton of large sharks.

Shark leather can be made up into shoes, handbags, wallets, purses, or other goods for which a high-class, durable leather is desired. Although perfectly pliable it has a very hard surface which renders it extremely durable. I have in my possession a wallet made of shark leather that has had constant use for over ten years and it has not yet shown the slightest sign of wear.

Although hundreds of hides were tanned by a Sydney tanner when one of the New South Wales companies was operating at Port Stephens and the manufactured goods had a ready sale, there is no market at present in Australia for the salted hides. There is a market for them, however, in London and the United States of America.

The fins, which consist of gelatinous rays, are cut off with an inward curve in order that no flesh may remain adherent at the base and they are laid in the sun on wire-netting supported above the ground. The time taken in drying varies according to the heat of the sun and the humidity, but is generally complete in about a week or a fortnight. The fins of commercial value are the dorsal (on the back), the pectorals (on the sides), and the lower (smaller) lobe of the caudal or tail fin. The value of the fins varies greatly according to the species of shark from which they are taken; they may be either graded or shipped as mixed fins. From twenty to twenty-five pounds of dried fins are yielded by a ton of sharks.

The oil is extracted from the livers either by means of direct steam or in a steam-jacketed kettle; the livers must be treated as soon as possible after the death of the shark for deterioration is very rapid. In the course of about four hours' steaming most of the oil will be found to have come away; it is run through a tap in the side of the container near its base and strained through muslin or a fine wire strainer such as a petrol strainer in order to remove any liver debris.

Soon after settling, a whitish deposit known as stearin will be found to accumulate at the bottom, the amount being dependent on the temperature of the oil; in summer it may be negligible or completely absent, while in the coldest part of the winter it may take up as much as a third of the volume of the oil. This stearin must be removed before the oil is marketable, at least in Australia; it must be extracted at a lower temperature than the oil is likely to be subjected to during subsequent handling, preferably by means of a filter press.

A ton of large mixed sharks yields about twenty gallons of liver oil. It is used principally in the tanning industry for rendering leather water-proof and pliable, and there is a market for low-grade oils for the tempering of steel. There remains much work to be done on the vitamin content and potency of the oil for it may be found that the oil from some common species of sharks has a high vitamin A and D content. The vitamin A value of the oil of the whaler shark (the commonest large shark on the coast of New South Wales) has already been found to be twice as high as that of standard cod liver oil. Feeding experiments with cattle have shown splendid results in Queensland, so that further investigation in this direction is fully warranted.

It is difficult to see how the flesh can be utilized profitably. Although there is a market for dried shark flesh in the East, it is very doubtful whether the price obtainable would offset the cost of handling, treatment, and freight. If converted into meal it is unnecessary to remove the oil for it contains only about two per cent, the operations consisting simply of steaming, drying, and grinding. Its manufacture into meal, however, is not likely to prove economical unless very large supplies are obtainable at one centre.

What, then, are the prospects of developing an industry within the Great Barrier Reef? We can merely repeat that it is dependent on a sufficient regularity of supplies, but if we must express a more definite opinion we can only say that we believe the catches, although perhaps at times prolific enough, will be found to be too irregular to allow of the development of an industry based on the capture of sharks alone. We hope we are wrong for most of us would certainly not be worried by their depletion.

But even if the capture of sharks does not develop into a major industry there is nothing to prevent fishermen adding to their incomes by exploiting them during periods when edible fish are scarce. The expensive equipment with its associated overhead costs necessary for the capture and treatment of sharks on a large scale will at least be avoided. Huge nets, such as those used in the industry in New South Wales, a thousand feet long and twenty feet deep, are costly, but the individual fisherman will probably catch all he can conveniently handle by means of hand or long lines, and although each fisherman's catch will possibly not be very great, if all fishermen were to engage in their capture during slack periods the aggregate catch would probably be very considerable. In addition, a service will be performed by helping to rid us of a fish that is certainly not desirable in our waters.

The commonest large shark on the Queensland coast is the tiger shark, though at times the whaler and the grey nurse may be found in considerable numbers. The tiger shark reaches a length of upwards of eighteen feet with a weight of at least fifteen hundred pounds. The grey nurse may grow to fifteen feet and the whaler somewhat less. The products of all three are valuable, but the tiger shark produces the greatest amount of oil. A thirteen feet tiger shark I once saw caught at Port Stephens had a liver seven feet long and it yielded eighteen gallons of oil.

SOUP FROM TURTLES

As was pointed out in Chapter VIII several attempts have been made to commercialize the turtles of the Great Barrier Reef. In January 1924 a canning factory began to operate at North-West Island in the Capricorn Group and continued until February 1928, when it closed down. The season extends (in the Capricorns) from the beginning of November till the end of February, for it is during this period that the female turtles come ashore to lay their eggs. During the first season's activities 12,000 sixteen-ounce tins of soup were marketed; during the three subsequent seasons the output averaged about 50,000 twelve-ounce tins, and during the last season's operations 70,000 twelve-ounce tins were produced.

During the 1926-7 season a factory for the treatment of turtles operated at Heron Island in the same group, and during that period produced about 25,000 tins. This factory then remained idle till November 1929, when a small pack comprising about 8000 tins was canned. Since that time there has been no regular turtle fishery anywhere on the reef, though a few turtles are intermittently forwarded alive to hotels in Brisbane and Sydney for conversion into soup.

The green turtle (Plate 26, fig. 2) is the only one whose flesh is valued as food, the others commonly found on the reef being rank and unpalatable. No males are ever used, not only because they do not come ashore, but also because their flesh, particularly that of the larger ones, is far less enticing.

The turtles come ashore at night, usually when the tide is high, and the hunters patrol the beach surrounding the island for their tell-tale tracks; these are followed till the turtle is located when it is turned on its back, for in this position it cannot right itself, and it is allowed to remain there till the following daylight high tide. The turtles are then loaded into boats or punts and taken to the jetty where they are transferred to trucks which run them into the factory. After decapitation, the flippers and plastron (breast plate) are cut away, the entrails extracted, and the flesh and the greenish coloured fat removed. The flesh, the fat, and the flippers are all used for the manufacture of soup; they are boiled in steam vats for about eighteen hours and then strained into concentrating vats where further boiling reduces the soup to the requisite density. It is then ready for canning.

Now, it is clear that the killing of the females before they lay their eggs, at a time, in other words, when their lives are most valuable for the propagation of the race, is extremely wasteful and definitely undesirable. If such a fishery were allowed to continue unrestricted it is inevitable that within a comparatively short time the turtles would be reduced to a limit beyond which it would be unprofitable to hunt them. If, therefore, any attempt is made to revive this industry it is obvious that some regulation against their unrestricted capture will be necessary. F. W. Moorhouse, who carried out an investigation of the turtles that visit Heron Island, was able to determine that most of those that come ashore after the middle of November have already been ashore to lay previously, and he therefore recommends that the capture of turtles be prohibited before the end of November for by that time all will have had an opportunity of laying at least once. The wisdom of this is abundantly clear and it is to be hoped that if the industry is re-established such a restriction will be enforced.

It is possible, of course, that the egg-laying season farther north may not coincide with that in the Capricorns, but, failing an investigation to determine accurately the period during which the turtles go ashore on any island or group of islands, there is probably sufficient information available from local inhabitants to form at least a tentative guide for the determination of a restrictive period.

But is it desirable that the turtle be exploited at all? Certainly the products, both soup and meat, are very palatable, but the industry is accompanied by much unavoidable cruelty to the animals. If we must have a turtle industry, however, at least let us so regulate it that the animals are not reduced to the verge of extinction as has happened to so many creatures man has exploited for his personal gain.

OYSTERS, CRABS, AND LOBSTERS

Although oysters are fairly abundant on coral rock and nigger-heads round some of the coral islands, and are very prevalent on the rocks fringing many of the mainland islands, there does not appear to be any promise of an industry developing from their cultivation. It is true that small quantities have been marketed from some of these situations during the past few years, but the rocks of the mainland islands, whence all the supplies have so far been obtained, are of such great hardness that the shells of the oysters break when an attempt is made to remove them. This has rendered it necessary to open them on the spot and to distribute the oyster meats ("shucked" oysters as they are termed in the United States of America) in suitable containers. On account of the hardness of the stone where these oysters occur, the use of it for artificial cultivation is impracticable, and the transport of suitable cultch to those areas is not justified, for the reason that the oyster is a very slow-growing type. When the naturally occurring crops are depleted it will be many years before another crop reaches marketable size.

But that is not all. The catch of spat appears always to be very light. In 1929 I landed, when the tide was low, on Ethel Rocks situated a few miles south-east of Gladstone, and found them to be literally smothered with oysters almost to the exclusion of other forms of life, but although I made a careful survey of the whole area the number of young oysters to be found was extraordinarily small. Most of them were a great age as was indicated by the successive depositions of shell along the hinge-line, and although there was no means of determining with any degree of reliability the length of time they had been there, a long association with oyster life generally led me to assess the age of many of them at possibly twenty or thirty years.

The reason for the poor crops is easily explained. During the spawning season the sexual products are thrown out into the water in vast quantities; fertilization occurs as they intermingle, and for about a week or more the microscopic larvae are able to swim about, but they can only swim feebly and are carried hither and thither by currents which may have taken them for many miles by the time they are ready to attach themselves and settle down to a sedentary existence. Now, the ocean is a vast place, and the surfaces available for attachment few and far between; the wastage is enormous and the chance of settling remote in the extreme. It is obvious, therefore, that in such an environment the crop each year will always be very small.

There appears to be no prospect at all of oyster culture developing as a Barrier Reef industry.

Two swimming crabs of large size, meaty and of delicious flavour, occur commonly throughout the Great Barrier Reef area, and, although fair quantities are captured for market, the supplies do not warrant an optimistic outlook for a great expansion of the industry, such, for instance, as would justify canning operations. For this purpose it is necessary that large quantities occur over a sufficiently restricted area to allow of their capture economically. These crabs certainly do not fulfil those requirements.

The gaudily patterned Barrier Reef lobster also occurs throughout the whole length of the reef and may be found at times in considerable numbers, but, again, its concentration at any one centre is never sufficiently great to warrant a prediction that its exploitation on a large scale is commercially possible.

SPONGES

Although sponges are abundant and widely distributed throughout the Great Barrier Reef, with few exceptions they are of no commercial value, and, although much exploratory work remains to be done, none appears yet to have been found of a quality comparable with the renowned Turkey cup sponge of commerce. Nevertheless there are at least three varieties that give promise of commercial exploitation, and one of them is of such a quality and texture that it appears to have distinct possibilities as a toilet article.

As a result of an investigation carried out by F. W. Moorhouse on the sponge resources of the reef it was found that these sponges are readily capable of cultivation by growing them from cuttings. One of them, black in colour when alive and yellowish-brown when cleaned, is found commonly on reef flats; the second, also black and somewhat coarser, occurs on the outer surf-beaten zone of the reefs; and the third, brown when alive and beautifully white when cleaned, is a deeper water species and was obtained by means of a dredge in about twelve fathoms. This deep water variety has a very smooth texture, is strong and tenacious, but unlike the others, which assume a roughly spherical shape, it is elongated and almost cylindrical.

It was found that if one sponge was cut up into smaller pieces and suspended from a wire stretched between two stakes driven into the sand in such a position that they were never exposed to the air nor allowed to touch the bottom, growth was rapid, their lineal dimensions being increased from two and a half to three times in the course of eighteen months.

s

Although the highest prices are brought for sponges suitable for toilet purposes, there is a constant and world-wide demand for those that satisfy certain industrial requirements, such as the washing of motor cars, and for use in the painting and printing trades.

Unless further investigation reveals the presence of rich beds over an extensive area there does not appear to be much possibility of a sponge industry developing on the reef without cultivation being resorted to, and Moorhouse has shown that this can be accomplished without difficulty. The potentialities of a sponge industry therefore warrant serious consideration.

At the present time the whole of the Australian requirements are met by importations from Greece and Italy, the product of the Mediterranean and the Levant, and from the United States of America, where the bulk of the supplies are received from Florida.

The sponge we use is but the skeleton of the animal consisting of a fibrous network, which supported the soft tissues of the sponge when it was alive. The living sponge is far more solid and has the consistency of tough beef liver, while the surface is covered by a membrane or "skin," as it is known in the trade. It is usually found attached to rocks or other objects, though occasionally it may be torn from its attachment by heavy seas and lie free on the bottom.

In the Mediterranean sponges are gathered by wading, naked diving, transfixing with long-handled harpoons armed at the tip with from two to five barbed points, dredging, or diving in a diving-dress. They are placed on deck and killed by repeatedly tramping over them, and they are then suspended over the side of the boat to allow the water to wash away the broken tissues, and finally they are washed thoroughly on deck in tubs of sea-water. They are usually bleached by chemical treatment, but, although their colour is improved by this means, their durability is seriously affected. When trimmed by removing irregularities they are sorted according to size and quality, and packed in bales for shipment overseas.

CHAPTER
EIGHTEEN

Flotsam and
Jetsam

FEW matters of outstanding interest remain for our consideration, yet this book would be lacking without reference to some of the features of reef life that have not
fallen within the scope of the subjects so far discussed.

To an observant visitor every day brings its surprises,
every day reveals something of interest that previously
remained undiscovered or overlooked. It must be realized,
however, that during the daytime most of the animals are
inactive and many take cover amongst the coral or hide
under coral boulders till nightfall, when they wander forth
to do their foraging. The search for these provides one of
the greatest attractions of a ramble over the reef. Every
overturned boulder reveals a mixed population that lay
concealed there, and the visitor who fails to explore such
situations misses many of the reef's richest treasures. A
dead coral boulder, viewed as it lies on the surface of the
sand, is drab and unattractive, but when turned over its
under-surface will probably be found to display a wealth of
colour, perhaps rich and brilliant, perhaps of the most delicate tints intermingled with pastel shades (Plate 8, fig. 1).
These encrusting growths consist usually of sea-mats or
lace-corals, while adhering to their surface will frequently
be found the eggs of many types of marine animals, some
in naked clusters, others protected by capsules or perhaps